PLANT LIST

OF THE

PITTOCK MANSION GARDENS

PORTLAND, OREGON

PANOPLY PRESS, INC.

Copyright @ 2013 by Panoply Press, Inc.
Photos: Copyright © 2010 by Dee Linde

ISBN: 978-1-882877-43-0

Printed & bound in the United States of America

Cover & text design: Heather Kibbey

Photography: The photos seen on the cover and text pages are the work of OSU Master Gardener, Dee Linde, who is determined to one day have photographed all the plants in all seasons of growth!

A Note about the Plant List: Just as the gardens at Pittock Mansion are in a wonderful state of evolution, so is this Plant List, which changes as new plants are added or removed. Fort this reason, we assign a number to the version of the list. Current version is #513.

Published by: Panoply Press, Inc.
PO Box 1885 · Lake Oswego, Oregon, USA 97035
PanoplyPress@gmail.com

ACKNOWLEDGMENTS

The restoraton of the Pittock Mansion gardens has been the work, the dedication and the dream of so many talented and generous people.

Robin Akers, our Pittock horticulturist, had the vision to create a significant perennial garden on the grounds of the Mansion. He would not have succeeded without the support of Oregon State University Master Gardeners—hundreds of them—who have braved unmentionably difficult weather at times, to provide inspiration and education, along with hard garden labor! Whether deadheading roses, answering gardening questions or leading "garden conversations," as we call our free garden tours, the OSU Master Gardeners have been an absolutely essential part of this experience.

There would be no "Plant List" book today if one Master Gardener, Skip Frankwick, had not spent at least a zillion hours maintaining a list of most of the plants in the Pittock Gardens. She even took it a step further and labeled them in the beds, so visitors can enjoy this garden to the fullest!

Thank you to the staff at the Portland Parks Department, the leadership of OSU Master Gardeners, the staff at Pittock Mansion, and the Pittock Mansion Society for support and encouragement in this continuing effort.

TABLE OF CONTENTS

A full-color map of the gardens can be found on the back cover.

PLANT LIST OF THE PITTOCK GARDENS, BY GARDEN, *continued:*

VISITING THE GARDENS AT PITTOCK MANSION:

The love of gardening...

is a seed once sown that never dies.

- Gertrude Jekyll

The Gardens
at Pittock Mansion

INTRODUCTION

There is no place that speaks to the spirit of Oregon quite like Pittock Mansion. One hundred years ago, on a hill overlooking the growing young city of Portland, pioneers Henry Pittock and his wife, Georgiana, built the home where they would spend the rest of their days. By the time construction was completed, Mr. and Mrs. Pittock were in their 70s. And what a home it was—unlike anything built by their Victorian contemporaries, the Pittock home is welcoming in its elegance and simplicity of design and detail. Surprisingly, it wasn't situated in the elite area of what is now downtown Portland, but instead was built on 46 acres of hilltop land that Henry had purchased, known as Imperial Heights.

An ardent naturalist, Henry insisted on using native materials throughout, with few exceptions. He encouraged local craftsmen to design such amenities as the light fixtures and to build the intricate wood floors. He filled the home with the very latest in technological marvels, such as an elevator for Georgiana (who was by then in a wheelchair), a built-in vacuum cleaner and even an automatic draining system for indoor planters.

There is no doubt that Henry was a consummate businessman and, as owner of the *Oregonian* newspaper (one of his many ventures), he and Georgiana were among the city's most prominent couples. Georgiana was an interesting and capable woman. Some of the many charitable organizations she helped establish, to provide care for the disadvantaged, are still active today.

But it's Georgiana's love of roses that has established her legacy and endeared her to gardeners. When she attended a lecture about roses in Britain, and encouraged her reluctant husband to accompany her on a tour of English gardens, who could have guessed that this would have such a significant effect on the city of Portland? She returned from her trip enthused about what she had seen and, as you'll learn later in this book, introduced the concept of rose competition to a city where gardens flourish. Georgiana deserves credit for establishing Portland as, most certainly, *The City of Roses.*

Henry and Georgiana lived only a short time in their home on the hill, but the Pittock family owned it for many decades. Finally, after severe damage from the Columbus Day Storm in 1962, the citizens of Portland rallied to purchase and protect the Mansion. Henry and Georgiana's 46 acres became a Portland city park. Since that time, the Mansion has been restored and is truly a Portland treasure.

The grounds, however, like many urban parks, went through a period of stagnation. When I joined Pittock Mansion Society's Board of Directors in the early 1990s, the landscaping was basic and uninspired. Each season, the City of Portland would provide hundreds of annuals from its greenhouse to be planted in rows— impatiens, petunias, etc.—the usual fare for park borders.

It wasn't until a few years later that several influences brought change to the gardens. The first was the establishment of the OSU Master Gardener volunteer program at Pittock Mansion, which I organized in 1999. We started that year with one Master Gardener, who deadheaded roses while answering any gardening questions that came her way.

The next year, several more volunteered, and I discovered that the OSU Master Gardeners loved to be in this magical spot, with views of the mountains and city, so recruiting was easy. Their numbers grew until in recent years we have had, on average, 75 volunteers a season. These Master Gardeners have brought to Pittock Mansion a wonderful knowledge of plants and of garden design, and they were eager to help nudge the gardens to a much higher level of sophistication. Many volunteers have faithfully returned, year after year, like the perennials they tend.

Another factor that led to change was the closing of the City's greenhouses and the loss of a steady supply of annual plants. In reality, however, those plants were "enablers"—helping to maintain the status quo, keeping the gardens colorful, but lacking the imaginative "draw" that surprises and satisfies us.

Several years ago, Robin Akers, the Pittock horiculturist, expressed his vision of creating a perennial garden that incorporated the beauty and sophistication suited to Pittock Mansion, a display garden that offered visual interest throughout the year, and a garden that gave nod to the historic roots of this magnificent property and its original owners. By the mid-2000s, he had everything he needed: a vision; a splendid setting; a crew of talented, hardworking Master Gardeners; and plenty of garden beds waiting to be transformed.

Since then, Robin and his team have accomplished exactly what they set out to do, and are still finding ways to add further delights. So come visit! Like every garden, it is a work in progress and, thanks to those who love and care for it, it is *very exciting* work to watch!

- Heather Kibbey,

OSU Master Gardener, Coordinator for Pittock Mansion

OSU EXTENSION SERVICE MASTER GARDENERS...

are in the Pittock Gardens to answer your questions about plants or sustainable gardening practices on Monday mornings from May through September, 9:30 am to 12:30 pm. (Not on holidays, weather permitting.)

From mid-June through September, they are available on Thursdays and Fridays, from 11 am to 2 pm.

Free garden tours are given on the second and fourth Saturdays of the month, June through September. from 11 am to 2 pm. No advance registration is needed. Come learn and enjoy!

THE ROOTS OF THE PITTOCK GARDENS

At the turn of the century, landscape architects were called upon by the newly-wealthy industrialists to create showplaces of their estates. The Frederick Olmsted firm, headquartered in Brookline, Massachusetts, was a highly sought-after design firm that created landscape designs for several of Portland's wealthy industrialists. The Olmsted account register reads like a who's who of Portland – Ainsworth, Corbett, Failing, Kerr, Ladd – all hired Olmsted to design the grounds surrounding their estates.

Clarence Coit Colburn, a landscape engineer who had struck out on his own after being affiliated with the famous Olmsted firm from 1905-1908, was hired in 1914 by the Pittocks to landscape the grounds around their newly completed 16,000 square foot home. He developed a free-flowing system of curvilinear pathways connecting the estate's buildings. Colburn's plan is a good example of classic Olmstedian landscape design as well as the Neoclassicist approach which was typical in the first part of the 20th century. However this plan was only partially executed.

Midway up the stairway between the Mansion and Gate Lodge there is a landing spot that marked the entrance to the Pittocks' main garden areas, accessed through a large, beautiful grape arbor. A quaint cobblestone path led to a breathtaking shock of roses arching skyward over the first of two adjoined greenhouses. The area housed a tool shed, potting shed, and cold frames. But the real eyepopper was four massive rectangular gardens, measuring 120' x 60' in total – two vegetable gardens and two flower beds. These beds, larger in scope than the footprint of the Mansion itself, provided bushels full of vegetables destined for the Pittocks' dinner table and baskets full of flowers that festooned from vases throughout the Mansion. Down the hill from the greenhouses were tiered rows of raspberries and loganberries that Marjorie Skene, the groundskeeper's daughter, remembers as "just delicious."

Henry was a naturalist who loved the local flora, including Oregon grape, sword ferns, vine maples, and especially the majestic Douglas firs. A good many of the Douglas firs that were planted after construction were nestled up close to the house, some of which eventually fell on the garage in a 1962 storm.

Henry Pittock was a key figure in founding the Mazamas, the legendary hiking and climbing club. He forged miles of trails through his acreage and had twig benches and rustic log railings constructed, making for a comfortable and informal ambience.

At the turn of the century, it was commonplace for estate owners to name their homes. Since the Pittocks liked maple trees, (their previous home, in downtown Portland, was named, "Maple Grove," with maple trees surrounding the entire city block), today a garden at Pittock Mansion is known by that name. Other gardens at Pittock Mansion honor the family's attraction to certain plants, from Henry's iris to Georgiana's roses.

With such extensive grounds, the Pittocks needed a talented groundskeeper. James Skene applied for the position of "steward" for the Pittock estate. As part of the interview, Henry Pittock took James Skene out to the point and, looking down at the ground below, asked him if he could plant an apple orchard there. James said, "Yes," even though he wasn't sure how to do it. He got the job, studied orchard planting, and gave Henry his apple orchard. At least one tree remains on the point and still produces apples.

When the Mansion was constructed, Georgiana had her cherished roses brought from her previous downtown Portland residence; many ended up being planted on either side of the Gate Lodge. Some of the roses Georgiana may have included in her garden were the popular favorites of the day:

- Cecile Brunner, a polyantha rose introduced in 1881, nicknamed the "sweetheart rose" because of its perfectly shaped, little pink buds,

- LaFrance, the world's first hybrid tea (1867), and

- Madam Caroline Testout (1901).

Under Georgiana's guidance, the first rose competition and celebration, called the "Portland Rose Society Fiesta," was held in her yard in 1889, and several times later. By 1906, a parade was added, and the following year, the name was officially changed to "Portland Rose Festival." As part of the preparations for the 1905 Lewis and Clark Exposition and the parades of 1906-7, mile after mile of pink Madam Caroline Testout (pronounced TestTOO) roses, and other roses as well, were planted along the parade route.

It is said that Henry Pittock enjoyed the location of his new home because of the outstanding and unobstructed panoramic views. With an almost 360-degree viewscape, Henry could survey the domain over which he had had such an influence and where he had made his fortune—timberland, sheep ranches, paper mills, banking, real estate, railroads and steamships.

- Sandy Japely, OSU Master Gardener

EVOLUTION OF THE PITTOCK MANSION GARDENS

*An Informal Partnership between Portland Parks and Recreation, the Pittock Mansion Society,
and the Oregon State University Extension Service Master Gardener™ Program
has blossomed into a very successful venture.*

Over the past few years, the gardens surrounding the Pittock Mansion have been transformed to feature beautiful mixed perennial/shrub borders, woodland gardens and glades, a rock garden, a conifer bed, historic fruit and cut flower gardens and coming soon, restoration of native plant areas and the old orchard and green house sites.

The latest evolution of the Pittock Mansion garden began in the late 90's when a single Oregon State University Master Gardener, took on the task of deadheading the roses around the Mansion, while being on site in this busy city park to answer gardening questions. Master Gardeners soon began giving tours or "garden conversations" to welcome visitors to the Mansion grounds. Every year, the number of Master Gardener volunteers has grown, such that over 1700 hours of volunteer service are given to the Mansion garden annually.

The partnership between Portland Parks Department and the OSU Master Gardener Program has allowed the restoration and development of the different areas of the garden, in spite of continued cutbacks to Parks maintenance budgets. Master Gardeners help clear the sites, develop planting plans, plant hundreds of new, different types of plants, inventory and label the plants and maintain the gardens, while answering visitors' horticultural questions.

The initial goal was to make the stroll around the grounds interesting to even the casual visitor, to encourage an interest in gardening, and to showcase the wide variety of plant material that can grow in Oregon's wonderful, wet and mild climate.

Where possible, plants with historic ties to the Pittocks are highlighted in developing the beds and in the tours and signage. For example, in honor of Georgiana Pittock—who had ignited interest in roses by hosting rose competitions in her yard and who was a founder of the Portland Rose Society—the rose beds, which not long ago consisted of a single row of disease-prone, older varieties of roses, have been expanded and reworked to include diverse rose varieties mixed with perennials and other shrubs.

Another example is the development of a fruit tree/vegetable/cut flower bed that represents the potager garden that the Skene family maintained on the Mansion grounds for decades.

Other factors that have influenced the development of the grounds are the addition of an automatic sprinkler system in 1999, paid for by a Parks bond measure, the elimination of annual flowers from parks as a budget cut, and a re-organization of Parks Operations in 2003 that encouraged neighborhood groups to take on helping to maintain parks to help compensate for continual cutbacks in City budgets.

A Visitor Experience plan, begun in 2012 by the Mansion Society, will help direct the further development of the garden and hopefully enrich the visitor's entire museum experience.

The partnership between the OSU Extension Master Gardener program, Portland Parks and Recreation and the Pittock Mansion Society has truly helped one of Portland's crown jewels shine even brighter.

- Robin Akers, Horticulturist, Portland Parks and Recreation

FACTS FROM THE PITTOCK GARDENS:

- Although the entire Pittock Mansion property encompasses about 46 acres, most of it is wooded acreage where Henry Pittock carved hiking trails that are still in use today.

- The developed area that includes the house and gardens is about 3 to 4 acres.

- While areas of Portland at lower elevations are considered to be at a USDA hardiness zone of 8b, the hilltop location of the Pittock Gardens ranks at about a USDA zone 6, with parts of the garden perhaps even lower.

- Henry Pittock loved grapefruit and originally planned to construct an orangerie where he could grow the warmer-climate citrus fruits; however this was never built.

- The original road to the Mansion passed in front of the Gate Lodge, circled the Point, and brought visitors to either the North Entrance or the Porte Cochère.

- Chemical pesticides are avoided through the use of careful garden practices.

- Many plants from the era of the Pittocks are not suited to a display garden that must be in bloom for long periods of time--which is one reason why today's garden cannot exactly duplicate a garden of that time.

The Plants
at Pittock Mansion

ABOUT THE PITTOCK MANSION PLANT LIST

This plant list was created as a training resource for Pittock Mansion volunteers, who are called on to answer questions about many of the plants in the garden. Frequently the list is updated to reflect new additions (and subtractions) to the garden. Since no plant is ever in its final resting place, many get moved—and moved yet again—before finding what seems to be the perfect home.

The elevation of the Pittock Mansion Gardens is just under 1000 feet, which in Portland is indeed quite a height. However, with the panoramic views come harsher weather conditions. Spring comes later to Pittock Mansion, and the winter winds and ice can be hard on plants. While Portland is considered to be in the USDA Zone 8b with respect to plant hardiness, 8b plants would have difficulty surviving in some of these garden areas. The rule of thumb at Pittock is to consider it roughly Zone 6 or less in hardiness.

This Plant List is organized by individual gardens; you'll find a full-color map on the back cover to help you locate each one. Within each garden, you'll see location information (such as front, mid, rt, lft) to help you find a particular plant. Keep in mind that many plants don't make an appearance until May, so if you're looking earlier in the year, there may be no sign of them. By late May each year, signs will be placed to identify plants. These signs are removed over the winter, then replaced when the plant reappears.

We hope that you enjoy your Pittock Garden experience and take time to enjoy the free garden tours that are offered June through September on the second and fourth Saturdays of the month, from 11am to 2 pm.

PLANT LIST OF THE PITTOCK MANSION GARDENS

🌺 ENTRANCE, MUSEUM STORE - Bed to the left (west) of the Museum Store and Restrooms.
(Plants are listed from left to right, starting from end farthest from Store.

GARDEN NOTES
- The bold print in the description indicates approximate bloom time.
- Annual flowers are planted at the front border of this bed and those next to the Mansion; varieties change each season.

	COMMON & BOTANICAL NAME	NOTES
end	Evergreen Azalea Rhododendron 'Snow Lady'	2.5 ft evergreen azalea with large, pure white blossoms in **early spring**.
back	Common Snowberry Symphoricarpus albus	Deciduous rhizomatous shrub native to 6'; small pink-white flowers in **early summer**. White fruits in winter, often bending the branches to the ground.
back	Rhododendron macrophyllum 'Seven Devils'	4-5 ft. Loose trusses of 2" pink to deep pink flowers **late spring**. Native to the coast of Oregon around Coos Bay.
mid	Flowering Spring Cherry Prunus x yedoensis 'Akebono'	Deciduous ornamental tree; single light pink flowers in **Apr-May**.
mid	Ferns (Adiatum, Arythrium, Blechnum, Dryopteris, Polypodium, Polystichum, etc.)	There are about 360 species in N. America—you will see many varieties throughout the grounds. Evergreen Sword Fern (Polystichum) is predominant. Others include Deer, Lady, Bracken, Maidenhair.
mid	Rhododendron 'Whispering Rose'	2.5-3 ft evergreen azalea with trusses of bell shaped rose-pink to cherry-red flowers **May**.
mid	Evergreen Azalea Rhododendron 'Hino Crimson'	Ht. 1.5 to 2 ft. Bright crimson flowers in **April-May**. (This is a common planting throughout the grounds—many varieties. Same genus as Rhododendrons).
mid	Hellebore Helleborus 'Brushstrokes Strain' 'Mellow Yellow Mix', & ukn var.	Herbacious plant w/ greenish-white, cream, yellow or purple nodding flowers that bloom in **late winter and early spring**. Often called "Christmas Rose" or "Lentan Rose" because of bloom time.
front	Mukdenia rossii 'Crimson Fans'	Slow-growing groundcover related to Heuchera. Large maple-like leaves emerge green and age to mid-green splashed with red.
front	Sedge Carex	Grassy plants in the family Cyperaceae, commonly known as sedges. There are over 2000 species of sedge … Unlike other ornamental grasses, sedges usually perform best in partial sun to partial shade in moist, well-drained soils.

	COMMON & BOTANICAL NAME	NOTES
on wall	Camellia *Camellia* 'Freedom Bell' Small 'tree' in back to the left of the window. Hose-in Hose form: Red flowers in **April-May.**	Camellias are considered an evergreen shrub or vine and can reach 30 ft, although there are dwarf varieties. The decorative, dark green leaves are thick, leathery, and arranged alternately on the branches. The flowers are waxy, bowl/cup shaped, can be single or double, white, pink, red or purple. Bloom time ranges from **mid to late winter** through **early spring**. Many varieties throughout the gardens.
on wall	Camellia *Camellia hiemalis* 'Chansonette"	Weeping form (under window.) 2-3 ft tall x 5 ft wide. Bright pink blooms in **late fall/early winter.**
on wall	Camellia *Camellia sasanqua*	(to right of window) Will branch up the wall has a more open, willowy habit of growth. Red flower **Nov - Jan.**
on wall	Ardisia *Ardisia japonica*	Dwarf evergreen shrub (in front) has small white flowers that develop into bright red berries. (The larger variety is at the front corner.)
on wall	Clematis *Clematis* 'Crystal Fountain'™	Blue-lavender, 4-5" semi-double blooms in late spring & again in **late summer**; aka "Fairy Blue."

🪻 ENTRANCE, WOODLAND - Including the area around the ADA parking and the bed to the left, behind the benches and down the service walk.)

GARDEN NOTES

The plantings farther down the entrance road, along the bank, are listed in the Entry Bank section at the end of the plant list.

Development of the Upper Woodland area, that this bed borders, was begun in late 2009 and is ongoing. The intent is to return this area to mostly woodland plants and West Coast natives – Henry Pittock's preference. The project includes recreating an original trail through both the Upper and Lower Woodland areas, starting here and connecting with the sidewalk at middle landing of the stairs across from the Gate Lodge.

	COMMON & BOTANICAL NAME	NOTES
across road	Western Red Cedar *Thuja plicata*	Evergreen trees across road, bordering main parking lot—planted in 1962. Foliage has distinctive odor when rubbed; many uses among Native Americans. Exists throughout the grounds.
across road	(5-6 shrubs, unidentified)	
bank end	Rodgersia *Rodgersia aesculifolia*	Large green hairy palmate leaves. White flowers in thick clusters along 1.5 to 3 ft stalks **all summer.**
bank end	*Meadow Rue Thalictrum uchiyama*	Clouds of large lavender flowers on towering purple stems.
bank	Oregon Grape *Mahonia*	Shrub w/shiny, holly-shaped green leaves; bronze-burgandy in winter. Bright yellow flowers (Oregon State flower) then blue berry-like fruit.
bank mid left	Gold-leaved Red Current *Ribes sanguineum 'Brocklebankii'*	Shrub w/light yellow-green leaves. Bright pink flowers in early spring followed by edible berries in **mid-summer.**
bank etc.	Coral Bells *Heuchera* 'Cathedral Windows'	Common planting throughout. Leaves vary from greens, silvery, purple and drk brown. Small bell-shaped flowers (pink, white, red) on tall, slender stems in **early summer.**
bank	Dwarf Blue-eyed Grass *Sisyrinchium bellum* 'Rocky Point'	4-6"x8" Semi-evergreen clumps of grass-like blades w/blue flowers on single stems throughout the summer.
bank	Pacific Coast Iris, cvs	'Coastal Glow', butter yellow; Hidden Asset','tan mahogany blend w/pink highlights; Munras', drk cream yellow; 'Wild Survivor', lt med blue.
bank etc.	Ferns	Over 360 in North America—many varieties throughout the grounds— see note in previous garden list (Entrance-Mansion Store).
bank etc.	Daffodil *Narcissus*	Throughout garden. Descendent of wild narcissus. Yellow flowers **in spring** on a single stem, have a central trumpet (cup) longer than the petals.

	COMMON & BOTANICAL NAME	NOTES
near ADA parking	Kousa Dogwood *Cornus kousa*	Deciduous ornamental tree, develops mottled bark; blooms in summer, bracts change from green to white to pink. Resistant to Anthracnose (a fatal fungus that attacks Pacific Dogwoods).
back 1st lg tree	Western Hemlock *Tsuga heterophylla*	State tree of Washington: Wood used as trim in houses: fresh cut logs don't float.
near hemlock	*Cyclamen coum* 'Something Magic'	Small round leaves w/a Christmas tree center and a silver halo; topped by rose-pink flowerson single stems in **Feb/March**. Summer dormant.
under lg trees	*Pacific Dogwood* *Cornus nutalli*	Native deciduous tree (between Kousas); Larger than Kousa & susceptible to Anthracnose. White or pink blooms in **early summer.**
	Douglas Fir *Pseudotsuga menziesii*	Throughout. State tree of Oregon. Native only to Oregon. Valuable timber tree; good for high shade but a messy landscape tree. Named for Archibald Menzies and David Douglas, 18th century plant hunters.
under large trees	Big Leaf Rhododendron *Rhododendron macrophyllum* Native to Coast and Cascades; pink flowers in **May**.	Rhododendrons occur in the wild all over the world and have been in gardens since the mid-1600s. Size can range from dwarf shrubs to over 40 ft trees. Flowers can be various shades of white, purple, pink, blue, red, orange and yellow, and up to 6" wide. They usually produce in rounded trusses with as many as 15 individual blossoms on each flower that cover the plant in April and May. Many hybrids have been developed and a variety is represented at Pittock. (Azaleas are of the same genus.)
behind ADA parking	Maidenhair Fern *Adiantum pedatum*	Soft and lacy evergreen fern – over 200 varieties. Will dry up and 'appear' dead if not kept well watered.
behind ADA parking	Inside-out Flower (Duck's Foot) *Vancouveria hexandra*	1 ft tall groundcover – non-aggressive. Duck's foot shaped leaves & small, white shooting star-like flowers. Resembles Epimedium.
behind ADA parking	Wood Fern *Dryopteris austriaca*	8- to 30-inch triangular blades curl out in a horizontal from to create a wide, low mat.
rt of 1st bench	Rhododendron *Rhododendron* 'Ramapo'	Semi-dwarf, ht. of 1.5 to 2 ft. Bright pink-tinged-violet blossoms in **Apr-May.**
rt of 1st & 2nd bench	Coral Bells *Heuchera cvs* (See ID signs for names)	Common throughout. Leaves vary from greens, silvery, purple and drk brown. Small bell-shaped flowers (pink, white, red) on tall, slender stems in **early summer.**
around lamp post & benches	Bethlehem Sage/Lungwort *Pulmonaria saccharata*	Low plant w/spotted leaves & flower clusters in **mid/late spring.** Many varieties here include: 'Mrs-Moon': deep blue; 'Baby Blue': sky blue; 'Berries and Cream': raspberry pink; 'Emerald Isle': pink to blue; 'Excalibur': silvery lvs; 'Northern Lights': cranberry/purple/blue.

	COMMON & BOTANICAL NAME	NOTES
behind L of 1st bench	Blue Tit Rhododendron *Rhododendron* 'Blue Tit'	Small leaf and small true blue flowers in **April/May**.
front L of 1st bench	Pacific Bleedingheart *Dicentra formosa*	Graceful plant w/fern-like leaves and pendulous heart-shaped rose/lavendar flowers on arching stems Blooms **throughout the season.**
betwn benches	Knotweed *Persicaria virginiana* 'Painter's Palette'	Large boldly variegated leaves of white, cream, red, green with blooms of tiny red beads alternating along 8-10" spikes in **late summer.**
betwn benches	Colorado Blue Spruce *Picea pungens* 'Glauca Group'	Very blue native conifer tree of Rocky Mts., color more intense in sun.

NOTE:
Under the Blue Spruce, you can see down into the Upper Woodland area. Visible are various ferns, wood violets, Tiarella, Heucherella, Trillium, and other woodland plants. Henry's Trail is also visible.

	COMMON & BOTANICAL NAME	NOTES
front	Foamflower *Tiarella cordifolia*	Low, spreading basal heart-shaped leaves w/slender spikes of frothy white flowes in **spring.** Good ground cover.
rt of 2nd bench	Sweet Woodruff *Galium odorantum*	Ground cover with whorl leaves and sweet fragrance. Small white star-shaped flowers in **spring and early summer.**
behind 2nd bench	Scarlet Current *Ribes sanguineum*	Shrub to 10 ft. Once prized for its edible berries, now mainly an ornamental. Lobes of unevenly-toothed leaves. Flowers hanging clusters.
behind 2nd bench	Double file Viburnum *V.plicatum tomentosum*	Tree/shrub grows 6-8 ft tall and wide. Lace-capped white flowers in **May,** upright on each side of stem (dbl file.)
behind 2nd bench	Goat's Beard *Aruncus aethusifolius*	Large sprays of tiny flowers held well above lacy,deeply divided leaves. Blooms in **early-mid summer.** Male & female flowers on same plant.
left of 2nd bench	Lady's Mantle *Alchemilla mollis*	Soft, hairy scalloped leaves retain light-reflecting water drops after rain or dew. Sprays of small, pale green flowers in summer. Self-sower.

NOTE:
At the corner, the bed continues down the service walk, on the right side, until the Glade.

	COMMON & BOTANICAL NAME	NOTES
rt end	Scarlet Oak *Quercus coccinea*	Large tree native to Eastern No. America; fall color of large leaves can be bright scarlet or nondescript; doesn't seed itself as much as Red Oak.
under oak	Elegans Rhododendron *Rhododendron* 'Album Elegans'	Ht. 6-8 ft. Flowers are pale mauve fading to white with greenish yellow spots inside on dorsal lobe. Blooms in **May.**
rt end	Coral Bells *Heuchera* 'Firefly' (solid green leaves, red flowers)	Common planting throughout. Leaves vary from greens, to silvery, to purple and drk brown. Small bell-shaped flowers (pink, white or red) on tall slender stems in **early summer.**

	COMMON & BOTANICAL NAME	NOTES
rt & mid	Gold Heart Bleeding Heart *Dicentra* 'Gold Heart'	Glowing chartreuse foliage with rosy-pink bleeding hearts blooming in spring. Goes dormant in summer & returns the following **spring.**
rt	Scarlet Monkey Flower *Mimulus cardinalis*	Tubular scarlet flowers w/yellow markings in throat on light green foliage. Pollinated by hummingbirds. Blooms **July - October.**
rtl	Japanese Painted Fern *Athyrium nipponicum* 'Pictum'	Silver-gray 'metallic' fronds with garnet colored veins.
mid	Bishop's Hat *Epimedium x rubrum*	Perennial, shade groundcover, bronze, heart-shaped leaves on wire-thin stems pink/red blooms in **summer/fall.** Other common varieties in this area, also.
mid front	Sweet Violet *Viola adunca* or *Viola odorata*	Native to Pacific NW. Dark green, heart-shaped leaves.
mid front	Hardy Cyclamen *Cyclamen coum*, ukn var.	Deep crimson rose flowers that resemble butterflies bloom on 4-6" stems over a low clump of basal round or heart-shaped leaves in **winter and early spring.** Plant goes completely domant in summer.
mid front	Menziesia *M. cillicalyn* var multiflora	Slow-growing shrub to 2.5 ft. Umbels of bell-shaped rosy-purple flowers **April/May.** Named for naturalist Archibald Menzies, a Pacific coast explorer w/Capt. Vancouver 1790s.
left back	Common Bleeding Heart *Dicentra spectabilis*	Large, soft-green leaves with lovely heart-shaped, rose-pink and white flowers on arching stems in **May and June.**
left end	Hosta *Hosta hybrids* 'Bold Ribbons', 'Emerald Tiara'	Many species & varieties (2 in this bed) 8" to 2.5' high, 1' to 3' spread. Leaves can be smooth or ribbed, sm or lg, tapered or oval, plain or wavy edged., shades of green from lt to blue-green, solid color or edged in white, cream or contrasting green. (Check ID signs).
under cherry	Corydalis flexuosa 'Purple Leaf' (aka 'Blue Dragon')	Fern-like foliage turns bronze-purple-dark red in late winter. Racemes of bright violet- blue, tubular flowers with white throats on 10" stems in **March-April.** May go summer dormant if not watered. Compact 8 x 24"
left back	Oakleaf Hydrangea, *Hydrangea quercifolia*	White flower in upright panicles in **late summer** turn pinkish purple as they age; long leaves resembling oak turn bronze-red in fall; full to half-day sun best.
left back	Oregon Grape, *Mahonia aquifolium*	Shrub w/shiny, holly-shaped green leaves that become bronze-burgandy in winter. Bright yellow flowers in spring (Oregon State flower) followed by blue berry-like fruit.
left end	Flowering Cherry unknown var.	Upright flowering cherry that blooms in **Apr-May,** much like those in Mt. Fuji bed.

THE GLADE - Bed includes each side of the grass glade. from the sidewalk to the retaining wall along the entrance drive. Plants are listed in order from top (sidewalk) to bottom (road) as on the Right/NW side or Left /SE side.

GARDEN NOTES

Some of the plants near the road or at the "bottom" of The Glade are more easily viewed from Henry's Walk.

This bed includes a number of Hosta and Heuchera, all from plant divisions from the varieties in the Circle/Shade Bed. The other predominate plant is Hydrangea, with each type of blossom represented: Mophead, Lacecap, and paniculata.

	COMMON & BOTANICAL NAME	NOTES
rt/NW side	Corydalis *C. shihmienensis* 'Berry Exciting'	Bright yellow fern-like leaves w/purple flowers **spring through mid-summer**. Unlike other blue/purple corydalis, does not go dormant during mid-summer. 10"x16"
rt/NW side	*Hosta* 'Abiqua Blue Edger'	Plant: 8"x18". Leaf: 4" x 2" with 7 pair of veins. Blue green in spring, green in summer.
rt/NW side	Coral Bells *Heuchera* 'Lime Rickey'	Frosted, ruffled leaves are a shocking lime-green. 17 inch scapes of small, pure white flowers appear in spring.
rt/NW side	*Hosta* 'Francee'	10 pairs of raised veins on dark green, white margined leaves w/pale lavender flowers on 28" scapes. 24"x36" (does well in full sun).
rt/NW side	*Hydrangea macrophylla* 'Nikko Blue'	5' x 5'. Deep blue flowers on old growth. Prune after flowering. Sun/pt shade.
rt/NW side	*Hydrangea macrophylla* 'The Original' Endless Summer Series	3.5' x 3.5'. 6"-8" mop-head blooms pink in alkaline soils and blue in acidic soil. Blooms **all season** on new growth - remove spent flowers to encourage rebloom.. Bronze fall foliage. Partial shade.
rt/NW side	*Hydrangea paniculata* 'White Diamond' (Novalis)	4' x 5'. Glistening white panicles held upright – eventually fade to parchment and pink. Sun/light shade.
rt/NW side	*Petasites japonicus*	Large round leaves on edible 3 ft stalks (vegetable in Japan). White daisies in early spring before leaves. Invasive and difficult to remove.
rt/NW side	*Hydrangea paniculata* 'Pink Diamond'	6-8' x 6-8'. Bold 12"x8" blooms from **mid-summer through late fall** emerge a subtle chartreuse, turn pure snowy white, fade to pink and finally turn a deep, rich pink as autumn approaches. Adapts to sun (best) or shade.
rt/NW side	*Hydrangea macrophylla* 'Twist n Shout' Endless Summer Series	3.5'x3.5'. Mop-head blooms **all season** on old & new growth. Lacy deep-pink centers surrounded by blossoms of pink or periwinkle blue, depending on soil type. Sturdy red stems and glossy deep green leaves turn red-burgundy in fall. Partial shade.

	COMMON & BOTANICAL NAME	NOTES
rt & mid	Hydrangea paniculata 'Tickled Pink' (1st Edition Series)	Glowing chartreuse foliage with rosy-pink bleeding hearts blooming in spring. Goes dormant in summer & returns the following **spring.**
rt/NW side	Hydrangea macrophylla 'Light O Day' (1st Edition Series)	Tubular scarlet flowers w/yellow markings in throat on light green foliage. Pollinated by hummingbirds. Blooms **July - October.**
rt/NW side	Sword Fern	Silver-gray 'metallic' fronds with garnet colored veins.
right & left sides	Polystichum munitum	Perennial, shade groundcover, bronze, heart-shaped leaves on wire-thin stems pink/red blooms in **summer/fall**. Other common varieties in this area, also.
NOTE: The Glade Bed continues with Left/Southeast side.		
left/SE side	*Cyclamen coum* 'Something Magic	Small round leaves w/a Christmas tree center and a silver halo; topped by small flowers that resemble butterflies in **Feb/March.** The plant goes completely dormant in the summer with foliage returning in early fall.
left/SE side	Bishop's Hat *Epimedium x versicolor* 'Sulphureum'	Delicate looking evergreen. Wire-thin stemmed, mottled reddish-bronze heart-shaped leaves with pale & dark green veins that become purple as the leaves turn greener in the summer. Small bright yellow flowers **March through mid-May.**
left/SE side	*Rocky Mountain Columbine* Aquilegia caerulea 'Origami Mix'	Lacy foliage w/blue & white 2" bloom with long spurs on slender, erect stems. **Spring & early summer.**
left/SE side	European Columbine *Aquilegia vulgaris* 'Leprechaun Gold'	A mound of ferny, variegated, green and yellow foliage with small deep-purple flowers in **late spring/early summer.**
left/SE side	European Columbine *Aquilegia vulgaris* 'Woodside Gold'	Golden springtime foliage gradually changes to light yellow in summer. Gorgeous bicolored blue and rose blooms from **May – August.**
left/SE side	Existing Hydrangea – need to ID	
left/SE side	*Hydrangea paniculata* 'Pinky Winky' (Proven Winner)	See description on previous page.
left/SE side	*Hydrangea paniculata* 'Vanilla Strawberry'	6-7'x4-5'. Large, cone-shaped blooms start creamy-white, change to soft pink and then to strawberry-red lasting for 3-4 weeks. New blooms **summer to early fall**. Sun
left/SE side	*Primula japonica, Primula kisoana, & Primula x juliana* 'Wanda'	Primulas obtained from Berry Botanical Garden fall 2010. **spring bloom.**
left/SE side	Alpine Bells *Cortusa matthiolii ssp pekinensis*	Obtained from Berry Botanical Garden fall 2010. deep pink flowers bloom in **early summer.**

🎍 CIRCLE SHADE BED -In front of Museum Store (Gift Shop).

GARDEN NOTES

Locations are listed as on GS (gift shop side) or WG (woodland garden side) Start at Crape myrtle at left end of GS side & move right.

	COMMON & BOTANICAL NAME	NOTES
center	Elegans Rhododendron *Rhododendron* 'Album Elegans'	Ht. 6-8 ft. Flowers are pale mauve fading to white with greenish yellow spots inside on dorsal lobe. Blooms in **May** (prolific throughout grounds).
center	Scarlet Oak *Quercus coccinea*	Large tree native to Eastern North America; fall color can be bright scarlet or nondescript; doesn't seed itself as much as Red Oak.
GS far left	Crape Myrtle *Lagerstroemia indica* 'Zuni'	Shrub to 12' with panicles of medium lavender flowers **mid-June to late Sept** (has not bloomed since planted!! – most likely needs more sun); hybrid of L. indica and L. Fauriei. Introduction from National Arboretum
GS far left	Brass Buttons *Leptinella squalida* 'Platt's Black'	(Under Crape Myrtle) Ground cover. Small, bronze/green/purple, fernlike foliage creeps to form a very low soft, fuzzy mat. Tiny round yellow/green flowers in **June/July**. Tolerates light foot traffic.
GS & WG	Hellebore *Helleborus orientalis* (many var throughout grounds)	Herbacious plant w/ greenish-white to purple nodding flowers that bloom in **late winter and early spring** (var know as Christmas or Lenten Rose.) Varieties are being developed with the bloom upright, above the foliage.
GS & WG	Coral Bells *Heuchera sanguinea* 'Firefly', 'Amethyst Myst', 'Choco. Ruffles', 'Obsidian', 'Mint Frost', 'Fantasia', "Midnight Rose", 'Starry Night', 'Sashay', 'Berry Smoothie', Kimono', 'Green Spice', 'Cherries Jubilee'.	Another plant with many hybrid varieties throughout the grounds (many in this bed) See ID signs on specific plants. Leaves vary from greens, to silvery, to purple and drk brown. Small bell-shaped flowers of whites, pinks, and reds on tall slender stems in **early summer**. Plants are generally grown for foliage, and most are evergreen.
GS left front	Bloody Cranesbill *Geranium sanguineum*	In the wild, geraniums cover the entire northern hemisphere and some of the southern. The varieties are endless w/different size, foliage and flowers. Most have a loose plant structure and dainty, five-petal blossoms **May-Sept**.
GS left	Hardy Geranium, *Cranesbill Geranium* 'Johnson's Blue'	This variety is 6"-12" and has magenta blossoms in **late spring**.

25

	COMMON & BOTANICAL NAME	NOTES
GS lft front	Bellflower Campanula carpatica 'Dark Blue Chips'	Clumpy perennial with inverted bell or saucer-shaped flowers that bloom gracefully **throughout the season (peak in June and July)**. Varieties of various colors, but the blue is the hallmark.
GS left	*Campanula x pulloides* 'Jelly Bells'	Large deep-blue bells atop slowly-spreading mat of bright green foliage 8"x 14". **Spring bloom** to 11".
GS front	Hardy Geranium *Geranium* 'Thundercloud'	Mound of deep purple foliage w/ white to pink blooms throughout **summer**
GS front	Bellflower *Campanula* 'Birches'	4-6"x12" Plants form a trailing mound of small green leaves, bearing sprays of bright purple bell flowers throughout **summer**.
GS front	Adriatic Bellflower *Campanula garganica* 'Dickson's Gold'	2"x12" clumping mound of golden, heart-shaped leaves with star-shaped blue flowers thoughout the **summer**. Not aggressive like other garganicas, so does not 'hold its own' against larger perennials. Sun to part shade
Border GS/ WG	Creeping Wintergreen *Gaultheria procumbens*	Low spreading evergreen shrublet along border. Small bell-like white flowers in **late spring** followed by red edible berries.
GS right front	Foamy Bells *xHeucherella* ' Stoplight'	A hybrid cross between Heucheras and Tiarellas, so has characteristics of each. This variety has yellow leaves with red centers. Short white flowers in **spring**.
GS/ WG	Varigated Foamflower *Tiarella* 'Mystic Mist'	Bright green leaves with white speckled variegation and prominent red veins. White foam flowers in **spring**. Fall color has striking pink tones.
GS & WG	Hosta hybrids (see ID signs) 'Abique Blue Edger','Bold Ribbons' 'Emerald Tiara','Francee','Gold Standard','Golden Tiara', 'Invincible','June','Lake Port Blue' 'Regal Splendor','Samurai','Shogun'	Throughout—smaller variety on WG side. Many species and varieties (14 in this bed alone) 8" to 2.5' high and can spread from 1 to 3 feet. Leaves can be smooth or ribbed, sm or lg, tapered or oval, plain or wavy edged, shades of green from lt to blue-green of solid color or edged in white, cream or contrasting green. Primarily a shade plant, but some varieties are able to tolerate some sun.
GS mid WG	Sweet Box *Sarcococca confusa*	Dense shrub. Dark green, lance-shaped, leathery leaves – can grow to 6 ft. Small whitish, fragrant flower and berry-like black fruit-**winter**.
GS mid	Stinking Hellebore *Helleborus foetidus*	Deeply divided leaves forming loose rosettes through the **summer and fall**. The bell-shaped green flowers develop a purple rim.
GS center	Chinese Fairy Lantern or Fairy Bells *Disporopsis pernyi*	Evergreen spreader – 1 ft. Shiny dark green leaves and lemon-scented flowers that are flared at the tips. Flowers in **early summer**.
GS front center	Lady's Mantle *Alchemilla mollis*	Soft, hairy scalloped leaves retain light-reflecting water drops after rain or dew. Has sprays of small, pale green flowers in **summer**. Self-sower.
GS & WG	Ferns: Sword, Lady's,etc	As noted in previous beds.

	COMMON & BOTANICAL NAME	NOTES
WG left mid	Dwarf Sweet Box Sarcococca hookeriana var. humilis	Same as non-dwarf, but leaves are more glossy and max height is 2 ft – makes a good ground cover.
WG left & right	*Tiarella* 'Crow Feathers'	8", clumping, lobed bright green leaves with black feather and pink flowers to 12" in **spring**. Winter color a brocade of pinks, reds, purples, and blacks.
WG mid center	Gold Heart Bleeding Heart *Dicentra* 'Gold Heart'	Glowing chartreuse foliage with rosy-pink bleeding hearts blooming in **spring**. Goes dormant in summer & returns the following spring.
WG mid center	*Corydalis elata*	Elegant clump of lacy yellow-green leaves, bearing upright stems with dangling tubular flowers of bright, true blue. Fragrant flowering from **spring into summer**. 16" x 12"
WG mid center	*Brunnera macrophylla* 'Emerald Mist'	Silver dusting covering heart-shaped leaves with silver bars connecting to form a collar around the perimeter of the leaf. Blue Forget-me-not-like flowers in **spring**.
WG mid center	*Brunnera macrophylla* 'Looking Glass'	Almost solidly silvery, heart-shaped basal leaves w/minimal green veining (3"-5" wide). Blue Forget-me-not flowers to 18" in **spring**.
WG mid center	*Brunnera macrophylla* 'Jack Frost'	Silvery white leaves w/distinctive green primary and secondary veins, edged w/a thin green rim. Blue for-get-me-not flowers to 18" in **early spring**.
WG	Variegated Japanese Sedge *Carex oshimensis* 'Evergold'	8"x12" Grasslike evergreen. Low cascading clump of leathery green leaves, with a bright creamy-yellow stripe down the centre. Insignificant flowers.
WG front	*Tiarella* 'Mystic Mist'	5"x10" Bright green leaves with white speckled variegation and prominent red veins all year. In the Autumn the foliage gets striking pink tones. White foaming flowers cover the foliage in **spring**.
WG left & right	Astilbe *Astilbe x arendsii* 'Bridal Veil'	Airy pinnate foliage w/erect fluffy plumes of tiny flowers that bloom in **early summer** but last. Many varieties (colors & size) Bridal Veil is white
WG left & right	Japanese Forest Grass *Hakonechloa macra* 'Aureola'	Ornamental grass. Graceful arching leaves yellow w/stripes of green forming clumps to 14" high. Tolerates dense shade as well as sun.
WG right	Hellebore *Helleborus* 'Brushstrokes Strain'	Blossoms have brushstroke splashes, spots & true, rich colors (green, cream, purple) that adorn wide petals in **late winter and early spring**.
WG right	Hellebore *Helleborus* 'Mellow Yellow Mix'	Single yellow blossoms w/occasional apricot – some splashed w/picotee edges. Bloom in **late winter and early spring**.
WG right	Bleeding heart *Dicentra spectabilis* 'Alba'	Ferny foliage w/white, pendulous, heart-shaped flowers blooming on arching stems in **late spring**. Other varieties/colors throughout grounds.

❦ PITTOCK SIGN BED -Beside and behind the Pittock Mansion sign; when facing the Mansion, to the right of the entrance walk.

GARDEN NOTES

Includes plants in the area around and behind the sign, between the service entrance walk and the front entrance walk, from the sign to the end of rhe bed nearest the Mansion. Those plants visible from the service walk are designated "back side."

	COMMON & BOTANICAL NAME	NOTES
right at end	Coral Bells *Heuchera* 'Firefly' (green leaves, red flowers)	Heuchera are a common planting throughout. Leaves vary from greens, to silvery, to purple and drk brown. Small bell-shaped flowers (pink, white or red) on tall slender stems in **early summer.**
	Penstemon heterophyllus 'Margareta Bop'	2' x 2'sub shrub/perennial w/glabrous linear deep green leaves. Flowers in **late spring-early summer** w/ yellow-tinged buds opening to bright blue, rose-purple tinged flowers that fade to purple.
right end mid	Camellia *Camellia hiemalis* 'Tanya'	(Camellias are being introduced throughout the garden for their **winter** display – using mostly low shrubs and spreaders.)
right end back	Hardy Fuchsia *Fuchsia x hybrida* 'Santa Claus'	Semi-double white corollas with red sepals bloom **late spring to frost.** Prominent red mid-rib on the leaves on 3ft subshrub.
right end back	Daphne *Daphne x rollsdorfii* 'Wilhelm Schacht'	Small (12") evergreen shrub w/thick dark green foliage. Very free flowering fragrant pinkish-purple in **early spring.**
right	Cardinal Flower *Lobelia* 'Monet Moment'	3' tall spikes of deep rose-pink flowers through **late summer and fall**, over dark-green leaves.
right end front	Rose Verbena *Glandularia x Canadensis* 'Homestead Purple'	4"-8" high glossy green spreading perennial with branching stems. Brilliant purple trumpet-shaped flowers in clusters on spikes creating a round effect in **spring** & again in **summer**
right end back	*Oakleaf Hydrangea* *Hydrangea quercifolia*	White flower in upright panicles in **late summer** turn pinkish purple as they age; long leaves resembling oak turn bronze-red in fall; full to half-day sun best.
right back corner	Rhododendron *Rhododendron* 'Honsu's Baby'	Dwarf, light pink flowers.

	COMMON & BOTANICAL NAME	NOTES
rt & lft of sign	Dwarf Day lily *Hemerocallis* "Stella de Oro' and 'Happy Returns'	Narrow, sword-shaped leaves; single, funnel-shaped flower with broad petals and sepals. Many varieties (height and color.)
right	Evergreen Azalea *Rhododendron* 'Hino Crimson'	Ht 1.5 to 2 ft. Bright crimson flowers in April-May. (common planting throughout the grounds – many varieties. Same genus as Rhododendrons)
center of bed	Pink Dawn Viburnum *Viburnum x bodnantense* 'Dawn'	Upright deciduous shrub to 15'; clusters of pink fragrant flowers before the leaves from Dec.—March.
rt & lft of sign	New Zealand Flax *Phormium* 'Purpureum'	To rt and lt of sign posts. Sword-like, bronze (purple-red) ornament grass to 1.5 ft
behind sign	Dull Oregon Grape *Mahonia nervosa*	Evergreen, rhizomatous, native to 30"; yellow flowers, blue fruit; Chinese use roots for medicinal purposes.
behind -mid	Elegans Rhododendron *Rhododendron* 'Album Elegans'	Flowers pale mauve fading to white with greenish yellow spots inside on dorsal lobe; **May** bloom time.
back on left	Rhododendron *Rhododendron* 'President Lincoln'	Darker, flatter leaves.
left border	Corsican Mint *Mentha requienii*	Shade-loving perennial groundcover with small lilac flowers in **summer**; foliage has peppermint odor. Along edge of bed.
left	Garnet Penstemon *Penstemon* 'Andenken an Friedrich Hahn'	Semi-evergreen; spikes of wine-red, fox-glove-shaped flowers from **mid-summer to late fall**; best in full sun and good drainage.
left front	*Penstemon* 'Ruby'	Ruby-red flowers from **early summer to mid-fall**. Lush foliage on mounded clumps. 20"x18" May only live a few years
left border	*Cyclamen coum* 'Something Magic'	Small round leaves w/a Christmas tree center and a silver halo; topped by small flowers that resemble butterflies in **Feb/March**. The plant goes completely dormant in the summer with foliage returning in early fall.
left mid	Lemon Lily *Lilium parryii*	Small lily w/3" lemon yellow flowers – lemon scent
left mid	Rhododendron, Silver Leaved Yak *Rhododendron* 'Yak Van Zile'	Small. New leaves are soft-silver colored.
left mid	Winter Honeysuckle *Lonicera fragrantissima*	8 ft deciduous shrub w/small, fragrant creamy-white, pink-blush flowers on bare branches in **late winter**. Yellow-green leaves darken to blue-green and hold into winter. Bright red berries May/June.
left end	Rhododendron *Rhododendron* 'Christmas Cheer'	Mid-sized, **early-blooming**, PJM looking, light pink with spots.

	COMMON & BOTANICAL NAME	NOTES
left end	Camellia *Camellia sasanqua*	Dwarf variety – red flower **Nov - Jan**
left – far end	Rhododendron *Rhododendron* 'Carmen' *x R. degronianum subsp.* *yakushimanum*	Dwarf, deep red flowers
back side	Rhododendron *Rhododendron* 'Dreamland'	Mid-sized. Pink
back side	Fleeceflower *Persicaria polymorpha*	Large white astilbe-like plumes on ruby stems to 3-5' tall. Blooms in **summer.**
back side	Fairy Bells *Disporum cantoniense* 'Night Heron'	4-5' bamboo like stems bearing dusky purple leaves that fade to green as the summer lingers. Attractive tan bracts at each node enhance the bamboo effect. Nodding white bells in **spring.**
	Tree Peony *Peonea* 'Golden Sovereign'	5'x6'. Butter gold blooms in **late May.**
back side	Paperbush *Edgeworthia papyrifera*	Deciduous bush with bright yellow clusters of flowers at the tips of each branch in the **winter.**
back side	Fleeceflower *Persicaria microcephala* 'Red Dragon'	Rich burgandy velvety evergreen leaves marked w/lance-shaped mint green or silver chevrons. Topped w/delicate white flowers **Aug-Sept.**
back side	Rhododendron, Yak *R. yakusimanum* 'Angel'	3-4 ft. Shiny, glossy leaves, pale-pink, near white blooms **late spring, early summer.**

🦋 MT. FUJI BED - From Museum Store (Gift Shop) to Porte Cochère, under the Mt. Fuji cherry trees.

GARDEN NOTES

Plants are listed in three sections:
- along wall
- around water fountains (WF)
- under cherry trees

	COMMON & BOTANICAL NAME	NOTES
wall front & side	Boston Ivy *Parthenocissus tricuspidala*	Root-like tendrilscling to unpainted masonary surfaces with disk-like pads. Shiny green leaves turn bright red in fall. Inconspicuous flowers & blue/black berries.
left back	Preston Lilac *Syringa.x prestoniae* 'James Macfarlane'	Alongside Gift Shop; pale lavendar flowers in panicles in **May**; not fragrant
left back	Shining Oregon Grape *Mahonia aquifolium*	Evergreen native to 8' with yellow blooms in **late Winter—early pring**; edible blue-black berries, purple bronze leaves in Fall/Winter.
left back	Kousa Dogwood *Cornus kousa*	Deciduous ornamental tree, develops mottled bark; blooms in summer, later than Eastern Dogwood, bracts change from green to white to pink.
left mid	Dwarf Korean Lilac *Syringa palibiniana*	Upright deciduous broadleaf shrub. Usual height 4 feet, but may reach 8. Has fragrant, purple-lilac flowers in **late spring**. Needs full sun.
left mid	Daylily *Hemerocallis* 'Romulus'	Daylilies have a regular succession of large, funnel shaped flowers, often fragrant, each lasting one day, with many hybrid varieties of size, color (no blue or pure white) with **early/mid/late** blooming seasons. Romulus is black-red.
left mid	French (aka Spanish) Lavender *Lavandula stoechas* 'Blue Star'	Distinguished from other lavenders by its unusual flower blossoms which are tufted and pineapple shaped. Heavy bloomer during **spring** and needs to be cut back after flowering to maintain its shape.
left front	Fat Bud French hybrid Lavender *Lavandula x intermedia* 'Grosso'	Classic lavender used in sachets, perfumes, etc. Rounded habit, to 24" tall; foliage is aromatic and grey-green and deep, dark violet flowers appear on long spikes in **July and August**. Thrives in full sun and loose, well-drained soil. Little to no fertilization best. Prune soon after flowering to control..
left front	English Lavender *Lavandula agustifolia* 'Premier'	Low, grey-green evergreen shrub 24"x30". Space between the whorls of flowers on the long stems, give them an airy appearance. The calyx color is dark purple; the corolla is violet. Blooms in **early summer and autumn**.

	C<small>OMMON</small> & B<small>OTANICAL</small> N<small>AME</small>	N<small>OTES</small>
left front	New England Aster *Aster novae-angliae* 'Purple Dome'	2'x2', A naturally compact form with deep purple flowers in **August and September**.
WF Lt front	Speedwell *Veronica spicata* 'Royal Candles	Good cut flower – widely grown for spikes of small, close-set flowers blooming from **mid to late summer**.
WF lft front	Sedge *Carex elata* 'Aurea' or 'Bowles Golden'	2.5'x1.5' grass clump with narrow, bright yellow, lance-shaped leaves. There are over 2000 species of sedge. Unlike other ornamental grasses, sedges usually perform best in partial sun to partial shade in moist, well-drained soils.
WF lft & rt -front	Avens or Geum *Geum* 'Werner Arends"	Atractive basal leaved foliage with electric colored blossoms of red orange or yellow from **late spring through summer**. Good for cutting.
WF behind front	Dwarf Blue English Lavender *Lavandula agustifolia* 'Thumbelina Leigh'	Blue-green foliage to 12-15" x 18". Heavy bloomer; plump, compact flower heads of deep purple-blue calyxes and dark lavender flowers on sturdy, well-branched stems in **late spring**.
WF	Beard-tongue *Penstemon digitalis* 'Husker Red'	Spikes of red foxglove-shaped flowers in **mid to late summer** on 1.5 to 2 ft plant
WF behind	Gayfeather *Liatris spicata* 'Kobold'	Bold flowers 2 to 4 ft tall, **summer to fall**. Stems covered with clusters of tiny flowers that open and fade gradually from top to bottom. Good cut flower
WF behind	Salvia *S. x superba* 'May Night'	Slender spikes of small violet-purple flowers that bloom throught the **summer**. Good for cutting and drying.
WF behind rt	Yarrow *Achillea*	Fern-like foliage w/long lasting flowers with flat-topped heads that bloom in **summer** and will rebloom if deadheaded.
WF rt front	Speedwell *Veronica spicata* 'Red Fox'	Good cut flower – widely grown for spikes of small, close-set flowers blooming from **mid to late summer**.
WFRt mid	Pieris or Andromeda *Pieris japonica* 'Cavatine','Prelude'	Dwarf shrub to 3' white blossoms in **late winter/early spring**. 'Prelude' is whiter than 'Cavatine'.
WF rt mid	Dwarf Shasta *DaisyChrysanthemum x (or Leucanthemum superbum)* 'Silver Princess'	A dwarf (12-15"), compact mounded Shasta with large, single white daisies from **June to August**.
WF rt mid & front	Sea Holly *Eryngium* 'Sapphire Blue'	A coarse, thistle-like, clump-forming plant with basal rosettes of 4" serrate steel-blue leaves. Many tiny, stemless, steel-blue flowers tightly packed into egg-shaped heads atop collars of narrow, spiky, 1 in long blue-green bracts, rise in branched clusters on 30" stems in **summer**.

	COMMON & BOTANICAL NAME	NOTES
WF rt front	Shasta Daisy *Chrysanthemum*	Dwarf, white, **summer** bloom. Good for cutting.
WF rt mid	Oriental Poppy *Papaver Orientale* 'Turken Louis'	Crepe-paper like 4-6 inch orange-red fringed poppy flowers have a velvety black seed capsule in the center surrounded by dark purple stamens. They bloom in **May and June** on 30-36 inch tall stems and prefer full sun .
WF rt mid	Garden Sage *Salvia nemorosa* 'May Night'	Compact, clump forming plant of aromatic, oblong leaves and long spikey violet-blue flowers on 18" purple-red stems. Will bloom **all summer into the fall** if deadheaded.
WF rt edge	*Heuchera* 'Lipstick'	10"x12" Soft apple green foliage veiled with silvery white. Compact with a deep red flowers to 12" that rebloom over a long period!
WF rt back	Bugbane *Actaea* (formerly *Cimicifuga*) Need to identify specific variety	Has narrow spikes of small pink or white flowers, like elongated bottlebrushes, over 2'clumps of shiny, dark, deeply toothed leaflets from **mid-summer – fall**. Flower spikes range from 4 to 7 feet tall.
WF rt back	Delphinium *D.* 'Summer Skies'	Another good flower for cutting. Tall spikes in **spring**, may rebloom later in season. Usually blue but also other colors. Plant height reaches 4 to 6 ft.
WF far rt	Meadowsweet *Filipendula ulmaria* 'Aurea'	Low, lance-shaped golden leaves – full height to 3 ft. Flowers not prominent.
WF far rt	Rodger's Flower *Rodgersia podophylla* 'Rotlaub'	Bold palmate leaves w/jagged edged leaflets glossy bronze in spring. Has spectacular airy white panicles of white flowers rising to 5 ft in **early spring**.
back	Mt Fuji Flowering Cherry *Prunus serrulata* 'Shirotae'	Deciduous ornamental tree, single to semi-double white flowers in **spring**; horizontal spreading branches are characteristic of this graceful flowering cherry – canopy on a mature tree can reach well over 25 ft wide.
under trees	Small Solomon's Seal *Polgonatum biflorum*	Rhizomatous perennial, native to Eastern North America; greenish-white flowers in **spring**; enjoys humus soil and shade.
under trees	Foxglove *Digitalis purpura*	Biennial perennial, prolific self seeder. Pinkish-purple to white flowers on stalks to 5' tall; consider poisonous. Used to make heart medicine
under trees	Evergreen Azalea *Rhododendron* 'Hino Crimson'	Bright crimson flowers in **April-May**.
under trees	Alum Root *Heuchera micrantha*	NW native.
under trees	Foamy Bells	The snowflake-shaped foliage features blue-green leaves with dark centers. Warm pink flowers in **early June**.

	COMMON & BOTANICAL NAME	NOTES
BIRD BATH	See plaque regarding donor.	The bird bath, stone benches at the west entrance, and stone planters in the porte cochère were donated by a long-time visitor to Pittock in honor of her husband.
under trees	Varigagted London Pride *Saxifraga umbium* 'Aureopuntata'	Ground cover rosettes of varigated tongue-shaped leaves with tiny, pale-pink flowers on long stalks.
under trees	Primrose *Primula* 'Green Lace'	Yellow-eyed green frilled flowers from **April through July**. The petals seem to be made of leaves!
under trees	Black Mondo Grass *Ophiopogom plamiscapus* 'Nigrescens'	8"x12" clump of almost black grass. Although grass-like, it is actually a member of the lily family. Slow to start, but will form a groundcover mat over time.
under trees	Bugloss *Brunnera macrophylla* 'Jack Frost'	Almost completely silver, heart-shaped, hairy leaves with green veins. Bright blue forget-me-not flowers **mid to late spring**.
under trees	Heartleaf Brunnera *Brunnera macrophylla* 'Emerald Mist	Pronounced silver spots around the perimeter of the heart-shaped leaf. Silver, metallic-look dusting over the entire leaf. Baby blue forget-me-not flowers accent in the **spring**.
under trees	Western Sword Fern *Polystichum munitum*	Evergreen native, revels on north or east facing slopes; a very useful landscape fern.
under trees	Rhododendron *Rhododendron augustinii*	Evergreen, native to Western China; open blue flowers in **April–May**; named for Augustine Henry, an Irish plant hunter in China.
under trees	Rhododendron *Rhododendron rigidum*	Evergreen; pale mauve flowers with red dots. Native to China
under trees	Evergreen Azalea *Rhododendron* 'Everest'	Evergreen to 4-6 ft. Pure white flowers **mid-spring**.
rt end on column	Camellia *Camellia* – unknown var	
rt end	Annual Flowers	Different varieties planted yearly at front border

Mansion Entrance -Right and left side of west entrance.

Garden Notes

Plants are listed from far right to left, as right or left of door.
In addition to the perennials listed, different varieties of annuals are planted each year at front border.

ALOCACIA · ELEPHANT EARS

	Common & Botanical Name	Notes
rt & left	Flowering Cherry *Prunus* 'Okumiyako', 'Shogetsu'	Deciduous ornamental trees; double white flowers from pink buds on long stalks. Flowers after 'Shirotae' (Mt. Fuji) in **mid-Spring** .
left	Camellia *Camellia sasanqua* 'White Dove'	**Winter** bloom
left & rt in corner	Heavenly Bamboo *Nandina domestica*	Evergreen shrub new leaves are bronze in spring and turn red in fall. Clusters of white flowers up to 1 ft long in **mid-summer** and red fruits in fall and early winter. Barberry family – not a real bamboo.
right back	Camellia *Camellia cv*	Tall variety, single pink, blooms in **winter**.
rt & lft of door	Irish Yew *Taxus baccata* 'Fastigiata'	Right & Left of door. Narrow column when young; blackish-green leaves; shade tolerant. (Also far back on mid-right.)
rt back	Japanese Andromeda *Pieris japonica*	Evergreen shrub to 12' with white urn-shaped flowers in **late winter**; Also know as 'Lily-of-The-Valley' shrub. New leaves are rose-colored.
right back	Small Solomon's Seal *Polgonatum biflorum*	Rhizomatous perennial, native to Eastern North America; large grape-like leaf & greenish-white flowers in **spring**; enjoys humus soil and shade.
right mid	Hosta, cv	
right mid	Japanese Anenome *Anemone x hybrida* 'Honorine Jobert'	Hybrid rhizomatous perennial with semi-double white flowers in **late summer** on 3' stems. Can be invasive.
right mid	Corsican Hellebore *Helleborus corsicus*	Perennial to 4' by 5' with over wintering leathery leaves and green flowers in **late winter**; sun or shade.
far right	Western Red Cedar *Thuja plicata*	Foliage has distinctive odor when rubbed; many uses among Native Americans. Exists throughout the grounds.
far rt	Spreading English Yew *Taxus baccata* 'Repandens'	Long hedge-like planting under Cedar. Shade tolerant native of British Isles (a cultivar); seed in fleshy fruit is poisonous.

❧ PORTE COCHÈRE -Across from main visitor entrance (side entrance) to the Mansion.

GARDEN NOTES

The Porte Cochere, (or literally, *coach door*) is now the main visitor entrance to Pittock Mansion. The French term is pronounced 'Port CawSHARE' or 'Port CohSHARE'. The vision for this area is to create a quiet space where one could imagine Georgiana Pittock sitting to enjoy her private garden. Some of the plants listed below will remain; additions will be Kalmia, Lilac, Hydrangea, etc., and most likely, a rose….

	COMMON & BOTANICAL NAME	NOTES
left behind column	Northern Japanese Hemlock *Tsuga diversifolia*	Small tree in cultivation; hairy stems, slow growing.
left	Evergreen Azalea *Rhododendron* 'Hino Crimson'	Ht. 1.5 to 2 ft. Bright crimson flowers in **April-May**. (This is a common planting throughout the grounds – many varieties. Same genus as Rhododendrons.)
left	Evergreen Azalea *Rhododendron* 'Everest'	Evergreen to 4-6 ft. Pure white flowers **mid-spring**.
behind fence	Leiland cypress *x Cupressocyparis leylandii*	Fast growing tree with gold foliage.
back mid	Wintersweet *Chimonanthus praecox*	Yellowish-green Shrub to 9 ft. Opposite leaves have smooth margins. Honey-scented yellow blossoms open in **late winter** before leaves unfold.
back on fence	Siberian Iris *Iris sibirica*	Henry's favorite flower. Upright, clump forming, with masses of grassy leaves surrounded by many flowering stems – bluish-purple, small, but numerous.
back rt	Ironwood Tree *Parrotia persica*	Deciduous to 30', mottled bark, tiny flowers before leaves, yellow to scarlet Fall color.
back right	Anthony Waterer Spirea *Spiraea bumalda* 'Anthony Waterer'	Shrub to 3ft. Leaves have pinkish hue when young but turn green at full size. Bright crimson, flatish clusters of flowers to 6" across in *mid-summer*.
front	Hostas	Many varieties – see note in Circle Bed listing
front mid & rt	Lungwort *Pulmonaria cvs*	Many varieties throughout gardens. Low plant w/ spotted leaves and deep-blue flower clusters in **mid/late spring**.
outside on left	Lungwort *Pulmonaria longifolia subsp*	Another variety – note different mottling on leaves.
outside on left	Hinoki Cedar *Chamaecyparis obtusa*	Tall, slendar, dense columnar cedar - also called 'false cypress'.
outside rt & lt	Convex Japanese Holly Ilex crenata 'Convexa'	(Right & left, outside of Porte Cochere) Dense evergreen shrub to 5'; female clone. Hollies bear male and female flowers on separate plants (dioecious).
outside on left	DONATION BOX	Only specimen throughout gardens – note hidden slot on front under rigid top canopy. Thrives on frequent 'feedings.' Proceeds are used to enhance the gardens.

🌸 GEORGIANA'S NORTH BORDER -Across the north side of the Mansion, to the terrace steps.

GARDEN NOTES

Since this is a border with many different plants, they are listed in sections Right (R), Center, (C) and Left (L). Locations within each of these sections are described as back, mid, or front of the bed.

In 2013, a major repair project on terraces of the Mansion necessitated removing all the plants from both Georgiana's Beds – most of them can be found along the southeast side of the front lawn, and many will have ID signs – this list may be referred to for ID information, but not for location. The plan is to reconstruct the beds in the fall, once the construction/repair is complete.

	COMMON & BOTANICAL NAME	NOTES
	RIGHT SECTION	
R back	Hinoki Cedar *Chamaecyparis obtusa*	Also called False Cypress.
R & L back	Convex Japanese Holly *Ilex crenata* 'Convexa'	Dense evergreen shrub to 5'; female clone. Hollies bear male and female flowers on separate plants (dioecious).
R back & mid	Astilbe *Astilbe x arendsii cvs*	Airy pinnate foliage w/erect fluffy plumes of tiny flowers that bloom in **early summer** but last. Many varieties (colors & size) Both white & red here.
R back	Camellia *Camellia x* 'Elina Cascade'	Evergreen shrub to 10ft. Slightly pendulous branching. Pink flower buds open to 1" white flowers **late winter-early spring**.
R back	Saint John's Wort *Hypericum* 'Hidcote'	Golden yellow cup-shaped flowers 2" across on semi-evergreen shrub to 5'x 6'.
R back	Evergreen Hydrangea *Dichroa febrifuga*	A Hydrangea relative. Heads of lavendar blue flowers in *late summer* followed by blue fruit; an anti-malarial hence the "fever" in the name
R back	Tree Peony 'Hana Daijin' *Paeonia suffruticos* 'Hana Daijin'	Purple. Donated by Brothers Peony Nursery and Post Family.
R back	Herbaceous Peony *Paeonia*	Nine tree & herbaceous peonies in this bed – some have signs (Raspberry Sundae, Mt. St. Helens, Golden Sovereign, Hana Daijin, etc.).
R back	Common Bleeding Heart *Dicentra spectabilis*	Large, soft-green leaves with lovely heart-shaped, rose-pink and white flowers on arching stems in **May and June**.
R rt end	Lamb's Ear *Stachys byzantina* 'Helen von Stein'	A mat-forming, dense, white/gray woolly perennial. The large leaves are extremely hairy and very soft to the touch, thus the name Lamb's Ear. This variety does not bear flowers.
R rt end	*Dianthus* 'Rosie Cheeks'	2" pink, ruffly 'carnations' above compact mound of silver foliage **spring thru summer**.
R mid rt end	Carnation, Pinks *Dianthus* 'Raspberry Swirl,' 'Devon Suskin'	Compact plant w/narrow blue-green foliage. Flowers **late spring, early summer** - white-pink petals outlined by a rich red border and center.

	COMMON & BOTANICAL NAME	NOTES
R mid rt end	Cheddar Pinks *Dianthus gratianopolitanus* syn *D.caesius,cv*	Single form 1" flowers from **May – July**. Colorsrange from pale pink to magenta, often with a small white center. Foliage often blue-green.
R rt end	Silver Groundsel *Senecio vira-vira* "Dusty Miller"	Artemisia-like cut foliage woolly-soft to touch stays silvery blue year-round. Clusters of sulfur-yellow flowers at high **summer**. Sprawler.
R mid	Rose *Rosa* 'Cornelia'	Hybrid Musk. 6ft. Arching, spreading habit, dense dark leaves. Large clusters of rosette-shaped, dbl, pink-tinged flowers w/copper centers. **Spring-Fall**.
R mid	Rose *Rosa* 'Buff Beauty'	Hybrid Musk. 5ft.Clusters of double apricot flowers that fade to soft yellow. **Spring – Fall**. Prolific bloomer.
R mid	Russian Sage *Perovskia atriplicifolia*	Lavender flowers on long racemes on whitish stems in late summer; 4'x4'.
R mid	*Salvia nemorosa* 'Caradonna'	24"x18" Tall, very dark purple flower stems and stunning blue-violet flowers from **late spring thru summer**. Deadhead to extend bloom.
R front	Wallflower *Erysimum linofolium* 'Bowles Mauve'	3' x 3' mounding evergreen sub-shrub with mauve flowers **almost all season**. (2007-8 was a very good season for this plant, but since then, it has not fared as well – Extremely showy plant under good conditions.)
R, C, L front	Aster *Aster subspicatus*	Profuse daisy-like flowers – purple and blue shades massed. Frequently a **fall-blooming** plant, this is an early summer blooming variety.
R front	Rose *Rosa* 'Lovely Fairy'	Polyantha. Bright pink, 3' shrub repeated in both Georgiana's beds along the front border. Blooms **summer through early fall**.
R front	Speedwell *Veronica schmidtiana*	Deep colbalt blue spikes to 20" above tight 10" mound of thick silver leaves.
R front	Pincushion Flower *Scabiosa caucasia* 'BlueDanube'	Blue perennial variety; **April-June** blooms.
R front	Daylily *Hemerocallis* 'Happy Returns'	Daylilies have a regular succession of large, funnel shaped flowers, each lasting one day. There are many hybrid varieties of size, color (except for blue and pure white) with **early/mid/late blooming** seasons. (Happy Returns is light yellow.)
	CENTER SECTION	Cape Fuchsia, Peony, Roses, Delphnium, Hebe, Penstemon, Scabiosa, and Day Lily are also in this section. Different plants are listed below.
C back	Cape Fuchsia *Phygelius x rectus* 'Moonraker'	Tall pale yellow tubular flowers in racemes to 4' **summer**; semi-evergreen sub-shrub 3'x3'; full sun best.
C back	Cape Fuchsia *Phygelius x rectus* 'Pink Elf'	Dusty-pink tubular flowers , yellow interior has red edge - **summer**; semi-evergreen sub-shrub 4'; full sun best.
C back trellis	Rose *Rosa* 'Gertrude Jekyll'	English Shrub, DA. 6ft. Medium pink double blossoms **late spring & early summer**.

	COMMON & BOTANICAL NAME	NOTES
C back	Cape Fuchsia *Phygelius x rectus* 'Winchester Fanfare'	5ft shrub w/deep green 4" leaves. Showy tubular coral-pink flowers w/ yellow throat – **summer** bloom.
C back	Bleeding heart *Dicentra spectabilis* 'Alba'	Ferny foliage w/white, pendulous, heart-shaped flowers blooming on arching stems in **late spring**. Other varieties/colors throughout grounds.
C back lft	Gayfeather *Liatrus spicata* 'Alba'	White flowers in spikes on stems to 30" that open open and fade gradually in succession from top to bottom. **Mid-late summer bloom.**
C back lft	Crocosmia or Montbretia *Crocosmia hybrids*	Sword-like bright green leaves with vibrant flowers from **mid to late summer**. 'Jenny Bloom' is Mango color to 24", and 'Lucifer' is scarlet red to 36"
C rt trellis	Clematis *Clematis* ' Empress'™	Compound leaves on twining stalks that cling to supports. Pink/lilac/purple flowers that can be as wide as 6" – **summer to mid-fall**. Very Showy!
C mid	Rose *Rosa* 'Magenta'	Hybrid Tea. Mauve double blossoms **late spring & early summer.**
C mid	Delphinium *Delphinium elatum* 'Pacific Giant Hybrids'	Clumps of tall (4 to 5 ft) upright spires covered in cup-shaped flowers. Dark blue, light blue, or lavender, sometimes with a white or black 'eye'. Will need staking in a windy area. Blooms in **early to mid summer**. Good cut flower.
C mid Rt and Lt	English Delphinium *Delphinium elatum* 'New Heights'	3.5 to 4 ft dwarf variety have uniform flower spikes and a wide range of colors, eyes and bees.
C mid	Pacific Giant Delphinium *Delphinium* 'King Arthur'	Low mound of deeply-cut green leaves, bearing tall (4-6 ft) spikes of deep royal-violet petals with a white center. **Mid-summer** bloom, but dead-heading at the base will repeat blooming in fall. A biennial that may live longer.
C mid front	New England Aster *Aster novae-angliae* 'Purple Dome'	2'x2', A naturally compact form with deep purple flowers in **August and September.**
C front	Hardy Geranium, Cranesbill *Geranium* 'Johnson's Blue'	Deeply divided leaves on a mounding herbaceous perennial to 20"; lavender-tinted blue flowers w/pale mauve centers from **May to October.**
C front	*Penstemon x campanulatus* 'Sour Grapes'	Reaches up to 3 x 1.5 feet, with mid-purple, large flowers from **early summer to mid-autumn.**
C front	Yarrow *Achillea millefolium*	Short pink variety; rhizomatous and aggressive.
C front	Hardy Geranium, Cranesbill *Geranium* 'Ann Folkard'	Carpet of deeply cut chartreuse, trailing/twining foliage with saucer-shaped, black-eyed, dusky magenta flowers from **May to September**. Widespreading.
C front	Long-leaf Speedwell *Veronica longifolia* 'Eveline'	12-18"x15" Dense rosy-purple flower spikes **June-Sept.**, on sturdy upright plants with dark green foliage that turns red and purple as temps cool in fall.

	COMMON & BOTANICAL NAME	NOTES
	LEFT SECTION	Again, Hypericum, Hydrangia, Peonies, Roses, Geranium, Penstemon, Sage, Stachys, Asters, are repeated here, along with the Hanoki Cypress and Japanese Holly; different plants are listed below.
L back	Sword Fern	
L back	Siberian Iris *Iris sibirica cvs.*	Dark blue variety. Henry's favorite flower. Upright, clump forming, with masses of grassy leaves surrounded by many flowering stems – small, but numerous.
L front	Lady's Mantle *Alchemilla mollis*	Soft, hairy scalloped leaves retain light-reflecting water drops after rain or dew. Sprays of small, pale green flowers **in summer**. Self-sower.
L front	Russian Sage *Perovskia atriplicifolia* 'Little Spire'	Multi-stemmed, grey-green, shrub-like perennial to 2'x2'. Spikes of lavender-blue flowers **summer to fall**.

🐝 GEORGIANA'S EAST BORDER -On the east side of the terrace steps to the basement door.

GARDEN NOTES

Like Georgiana's North Border, this is a border with many different plants, and so they are listed in sections Right (R), Center, (C) and Left (L). Locations within each of these sections are described as back, mid, or front of the bed. Many plants are repeated from Georgiana's North Border. This bed has numerous peonies and roses. Of interest in the right section is the Oakleaf Hydrangia; the center section, the cardoon; and the potager garden & espalier trees in the left section.

In 2013, a major repair project on terraces of the Mansion necessitated removing all the plants from both Georgiana's Beds – most of them can be found along the southeast side of the front lawn, and many will have ID signs – this list may be referred to for ID information, but not for location. The plan is to reconstruct the beds in the fall, once the construction/repair is complete.

Most of the Potager plants were moved to the Veggie Garden near the Gate Lodge.

	COMMON & BOTANICAL NAME	NOTES
	RIGHT SECTION	
R & C back	Convex Japanese Holly *Ilex crenata* 'Convexa'	Dense evergreen shrub to 5'; female clone. Hollies bear male and female flowers on separate plants (dioecious).
R & C back	White Mugwort *Artemesia lactiflora* 'Guizhou'	4-5'x3' bushy, upright clump with red-brown stems and ferny purple-black-green leaves. Showy sprays of creamy-white flowers **late summer thru fall.**
R back	Oakleaf Hydrangea *Hydrangea quercifolia* 'Snow Queen'	White flower in upright panicles in **late summer**; leaves turn bronze-red in fall; full to half-day sun best.
R back & mid	Astilbe *Astilbe x arendsii* cvs	Airy pinnate foliage w/erect fluffy plumes of tiny flowers that bloom in *early summer* but last. Many varieties (colors & size) Deep red and white in this bed..
across walk	Fothergilla *Fothergilla* major	Deciduous, native to SE US; honey scented, white, bottlebrush flowers in *spring*, red fall color.
across walk	Fothergilla *Fothergilla* 'Blue Shadow'	Shrub with rounded blue leaves that turn to purple/red/orange in fall. 2" bottlebrush ivory flowers decorate the tips in **April**.
R, C trellis	Rose *Rosa* 'Gertrude Jekyll'	English Shrub, DA. 6ft. Medium pink double blossoms **late spring & early summer.**
R, C trellis	Clematis *Clematis* 'Empress'™	Compound leaves on twining stalks that cling to supports. Pink/lilac/purple flowers that can be as wide as 6" – **summer to mid-fall**.
R, C mid left	Gayfeather *Liatrus spicata* 'Alba'	White flowers in spikes on stems to 30" that open open and fafdae gradually in succession from top to bottom. **Mid-late summer** bloom.
R, C mid & front	Peony *Paeonia*	Thirteen herbaceous and tree peony plants in this bed – some have signs (Raspberry Sundae, Pink Parfait, Golden Sovereign, Mt. St. Helens, Hana Daijin, etc.).
R, C mid	Siberian Iris *Iris sibirica* cvs.	Dark red violet and white shades. Henry's favorite flower. Upright, clump forming, with masses of grassy leaves and many flowering stems in **spring**.

	COMMON & BOTANICAL NAME	NOTES
R mid	Crocosmia or Montbretia *Crocosmia* hybrids	Sword-like bright green leaves w/ vibrant flowers from **mid to late summer.** 'Jenny Bloom' is Mango color to 24", and 'Lucifer' is scarlet red to 36"
R front	Aster *Aster subspicatus*	Profuse daisy-like flowers – purple and blue shades massed. Frequently a fall blooming plant, this is an **early summer** blooming variety.
R front	Hosta *Hosta laevigata cv.*	Recently discovered species from Korea with **very late summer** spider-like violet flowers on 2' stems.
R & L front	Lavender *Lavandula x intermedia* 'Grosso'	Long silvery gray leaves; mid blue flowers open in **July** on this 3' plant; grown commercially for lavender oil. L.x angustifolia 'Hidcote'also represented.
R & C front	Daylily *Hemerocallis* 'Romulus'	Daylilies have a regular succession of large, funnel shaped flowers, often fragrant, each lasting one day, with many hybrid varieties of size, color (no blue or pure white) with **early/mid/late** blooming seasons. Romulus is blk-red.
R, C front	Russian Sage *Perovskia atriplicifolia* 'Little Spire'	Multi-stemmed, grey-green, shrub-like perennial to 2'x2'. Spikes of lavender-blue flowers **summer to fall.**
R, C	*Rosa* "Lovely Fairy"	Polyantha bright pink, 3'. Shrub type at front borders.
	CENTER SECTION	Peonies, Roses. Daylilies, Sage,and Lavendar are repeated in this section.
C back	Cardoon *Cynara cardunculus*	The ULTIMATE thistle – same genus as artichoke. Height to 5+ ft with hugh horizontal, silver-grey leaves nearly 24" long and 14" wide. Rich purple flowers on strong straight stems from **early summer to early fall.**
C back	White Mugwort *Artemesia lactiflora* 'Guizhou'	4-5'x3' bushy, upright clump with red-brown stems and ferny purple-black-green leaves. Showy sprays of creamy-white flowers **late summer thru fall.**
C back	Cape Fuchsia *Phygelius x rectus* 'Moonraker'	Tall pale yellow tubular flowers in racemes to 4', **summer;** semi-evergreen sub-shrub 3'x3'; full sun best.
C mid	Delphinium *Delphinium elatum* 'Pacific Giant Hybrids'	Clumps of tall (4 to 5 ft) upright spires covered in cup-shaped flowers. Dark blue, light blue, or lavender, sometimes with a white or black 'eye'. Will need staking in a windy area. Blooms in **early to mid summer.** Good cut flower.
C mid	Fox Glove *Digitalis purpura*	Biennial or short-lived perennial, prolific self seeder. Pinkish-purple to white flowers on stalks to 5' tall; consider poisonous. Used to make heart medicine
C mid	Tree Peony 'Hana Daijin' *Paeonia suffruticosa*	Purple Donated by Brothers Peony Nursery and Post Family.
C mid	Saint John's Wort *Hypericum* 'Hidcote'	Golden yellow cup-shaped flowers 2" across on semi-evergreen shrub to 5'x 6'.
C back	Clematis *Clematis* ' Empress'™	Twining in window. Compound leaves on twining stalks that cling to supports. Pink/lilac/purple flowers that can be as wide as 6", **summer to mid-fall.**

	COMMON & BOTANICAL NAME	NOTES
C mid	Rose *Rosa* 'Cornelia'	Hybrid Musk. 6ft. Arching, spreading habit, dense dark leaves. Large clusters of rosette-shaped, dbl, pink-tinged flowers w/copper centers, **spring-fall.**
C mid	Rose Rosa 'Buff Beauty'	Hybrid Musk. 5ft. Clusters of double apricot flowers that fade to soft yellow, **spring – fall.**
C front	Aster *Aster subspicatus*	Profuse daisy-like flowers – white, purple and blue shades massed. **Fall** blooming plant.
C front	Hardy Geranium, Cranesbill *Geranium* 'Johnson's Blue'	Deeply divided leaves on a mounding herbaceous perennial to 20"; lavender-tinted blue flowers w/pale mauve centers from **May to October.**
C front	Yarrow *Achillea filipendulina* 'Coronation Gold'	Bright yellow flowers in flat topped heads on 30" stems in **mid-summer.**
	LEFT SECTION	Here a Potager (Kitchen) Garden represents the vegetable gardens on the property in the early days. Of interest are the two espaliered fruit trees. Annual vegetables will change each season; perennial plants are listed.
L right back	Sea Holly *Eryngium* 'Sapphire Blue'	A coarse, thistle-like, clump-forming plant with basal rosettes of 4" serrate steel-blue leaves. Many tiny, stemless, steel-blue flowers tightly packed into egg-shaped heads atop collars of narrow, spiky, 1 in long blue-green bracts, rise in branched clusters on 30" stems in **summer.**
L right mid	Coneflower *Echinacea* 'Gum Drop'	Large, intense bright pink pom pom held over the pretty pink petals and supported on the strong 2 foot stems. 2.5'x2.5'.
L right mid	Coneflower *Echinacea* 'Cranberry Cupcake'	Large double, cranberry-colored pom-pom balls of short-wide cupcake habit on compact plants 14"x20" from **late June through summer.**
L right mid	Coneflower *Echinacea* 'Lilliput'	Dwarf, compact to 18" well-branched with rose pink petals and dark bronze-orange centers. Numerous medium size flowers throughout **summer.**
.L right front	Coneflower *Echinacea pupurera* 'Pink Poodle'	Double 4in, bright pink, fluffy flower heads resemble those of a Zinnia or decorative Dahlia. The cone at the heart of the flower turns black as the seeds mature. 2'-2.5'
L right back	Bee Balm *Monarda didyma* 'Jacob Cline'	4'-5' True red.
L back	Espalier Pear (6-way)	(Anjou, Bosc, Red Bartlet, plus three unknown.)
L back	Espalier Apple (6-way)	(Gala, Yellow Delicious, Granny Smith, Red McIntosh, plus 2 unknown.)
L border	Dwarf Blueberry *Vaccinium corymbosum* 'Sunshine Blue'	Upright, compact bush reaching 3' tall, with blue-green and burgundy foliage in fall. Showy hot pink flowers that fade to white in **spring**, yielding large crops of medium sized berries.

❧ POINT WALK ROSES -Three sections along north side of walk from Mansion to Vista Point.

GARDEN NOTES

A sign in the 2nd section shows the location of mountains visable along this walk.

	COMMON & BOTANICAL NAME	NOTES
back	Convex Japanese Holly Ilex crenata 'Convexa'	Evergreen to 5'; female clone; Hollies are dioecious (have male and female flowers on separate plants.)
behind fence	Blue Elderberry Sambucus cerulea	Native, white flowers, blue berries in fall only edible if cooked. Down the hill is Salmonberry and Red Huckleberry.
behind fence	Red Elderberry Sambucus racemosa L.	Large (10-20 ft) deciduous shrub or small tree of the Honeysuckle family has multiple trunks with coarse bark. Many, small, creamy white flowers in large, conical-shaped clusters in **April.** Large clusters of small, bright red berries appear in June, attracting birds.
behind fence	Twin berry Lonicera involcurata	Native honeysuckle; 8' shrub with interesting yellow flowers followed by red berries grouped by two.
	ROSA VARIETIES (bed in 3 sections) Ck ID signs for names & varieties.	Landscape, hybrid tea, grandiflora, floribunda, and David Austin roses. Most roses were added in 2005 and 2010.
west end	Cecile Brunner (polyantha climber)	Small, double, pointed white - light pink. 17-25 petals/ bloom
	Azalea	
front	Carefree Delight (Modern shrub)	Medium, single (4-8 petals) bloom form. Medium pink, white center.
back	Long Tall Sally (shrub)	White or white blend. Strong fragrance. 11 petals. Average diameter 4".
back	Dortmund (Climber)	Single red w/white center. Strong thorns. (Extensively planted at the Internation Rose Garden.)
front	Lavender Delight	Mauve or purple blend. Mild fragrance. 12 petals.
front	2 shrubs located between Lavender Delight unidentified	Light pink with yellow eye and deep pink blotches on tips of outer petals. Fragrant.
mid	Collette (?climber)	Old-fashioned; pink

	COMMON & BOTANICAL NAME	NOTES
front	Seafoam (shrub/floribunda)	Creamy white. Mild fragrance. 35 petals. Average diameter 2.5". Very double bloom form.
front	Sally Holmes (modern shrub/climber)	Single creamy white from apricot bud, yellow stamens. Mild fragrance. 5 petals. Average diameter 3.5". Single (4-8 petals), cluster-flowered bloom form.
	Azalea	
	SIGN - IDENTFYING 4 MOUNTAIN PEAKS VISIBLE ON A CLEAR DAY- 2ND SECTION	Peaks are: Mt. St. Helen's, Mt. Rainier, Mt. Adams (all in Washington), and Mt. Hood in Oregon.
front	The Oregonian (Hybrid Tea) Aka 'Sight Saver'	Light pink. Strong fragrance. 30 to 35 petals. Large bloom form.
back	Heritage (DA English shrub)	Light pink. Strong, lemon fragrance. Avg diameter 3.5'. Large, double (17-25 petals), cupped bloom form.
front	Kent (modern shrub)	Semi-double, white/cream
back	Pat Austin (DA English shrub)	3.5' to 5' Copper, copper-yellow. Strong tea fragrance. 50 petals. Large, cupped, nodding bloom form. Occasional repeat later in the season.
front	Sophy's Rose (modern shrub, English)	Double, bright fuchsia pink
back	Gentle Hermione (DA English shrub)	4' Light pink. Strong fragrance. Average diameter 3.75". 41+ petals, in small clusters, old-fashioned bloom form. Blooms throughout season. Good cut flower.
back	Falstaff (DA English shrub)	3.5' to 5' Dark crimson red ages to purple. Strong, old rose fragrance. 110 petals. Avg dia 3.5". Cupped, old-fashioned, rosette bloom form.
back	Strawberry Hill (DA English shrub)	4' Light pink. Strong fragrance. Avg dia 4.75' 41+ petals, small cluster-flowered, old-fashioned bloom form. Blooms throughout season. Good cut flower
front	Rhapsody in Blue (Floribunda)	mauve/violet-purple 3x3
front	Miss Alice (modern shrub, English	Double, soft pink
back	Lichfield Angel (DA English shrub)	4' Cream. None to mild, clove fragrance. Avg dia 4". Large, very full, in small clusters, cupped, old-fashioned, rosette bloom form. Blooms throughout season. Good cut flower
front	Cherry Meidiland (modern shrub)	Single cherry red w/white eye
back	Charlotte (DA English shrub)	3' to 6' Light yellow. Strong tea fragrance. 100 petals. Avg dia 3.5". Double bloom form. Repeat later in the season. Susceptible to blk spot & mildew.
back	Teasing Georgia (DA English shrub)	4' Deep yellow. Med-strong tea fragrance. 110 petals. Avg dia 3.25". Cupped form. Blooms throughout season. Blk spot resistant.

	COMMON & BOTANICAL NAME	NOTES
back	William Shakespeare 2000 (DA English)	3.5' to 4' Crimson-red, fades to purple. Strong, old rose fragrance. 120 petals, small cluster-flowered, quartered bloom form. Blooms throughout season. Good cut flower
front	Noble Anthony (Modern shrub, English)	Double, medium red
back	The Shropshire Lad (DA English shrub)	4' to 6' (8' if grown as climber) Soft peachy-pink. Almost thornless. Strong fruity fragrance. 90 petals. Cupped, rosette form. Repeat later in season.
	THIRD SECTION	
	Unknown white	
back	Charles Darwin (English)	Double, rich yellow
front	Molineux (English)	Double, rich deep yellow
back	Michaelangelo (Hybrid Tea)	Double, yellow
front	Cliff's of Dover (Shrub)	Single, white w/yellow center
back	Jardin de Bagatelle (French Hybrid Tea)	Creamy ivory w/pink edges
back	Bebop (shrub)	Semi-double, cherry red w/creamy yellow or cerise eye
front	Chihuly (floribunda)	Double, apricot yellow blush to deep orange-red
front	Cherry Meidiland (modern shrub)	Single cherry red w/white eye
back	Collette (?climber)	Old-fashioned; pink
back	Lloyd Center Supreme (Grandiflora)	Double, warm pink
back	Cecile Brunner (?climber)	Double, pointed light pink
front	Seafoam (shrub/floribunda)	Double, creamy white
east end	Green Rose Rosa *chinensis viridiflora*	Unusual green blooms late spring/early summer, made entirely of sepals, not petals. Bright green foliage w/tint of red in new leaves – smells like pepper. 1833.
	False Japanese Cedar *Cryptomeria japonica* 'Elegans'	Juvenile foliage turns red-bronze in sun in Fall & Winter. Eventually becomes a small tree.

🌿 FERN BED -Behind park bench, under the Shore Pine trees.

GARDEN NOTES

Plant in this bed are listed from left to right.

	COMMON & BOTANICAL NAME	NOTES
	Vine Maple *Acer circinatum*	Native, deciduous, understory multistemmed tree; yellow fall color in shade, red in sun.
	Shore Pine *Pinus contorta*	Behind bench; conifer tree native to Oregon, Washington and California.
left	*Rhododendron* 'Shamrock'	1.5ft. Chartreuse flowers w/light yellow spotting – blooms **early to mid-season.**
middle	*Rhododendron* 'Lemon Dream'	3' mounding shrub – soft lemon-yellow flowers with wavy petals, sometimes double, in **May.** Rounded leaves w/ brownish orange indumentums on underside.
middle	Soft Shield Fern *Polystichum setiferum* Multilobum Group	Evergreen fronds nearly erect, lance-shaped, light green. More divided than species.
middle	Soft Shield Fern *Polystichum setiferum* Plumosodivisilobum Group	Evergreen. distinctive shaggy, moss texture and neat habit of growth. Young plants have a shuttlecock shape but, as clumps build up, the shapes overlap so the impression is more of a mossy mound.
middle	Robust Male Fern *Dryopteris x complexa* 'Robust'	'A hybrid fern 3-4' ; foliage mass of deeply divided, upright arching fronds with a ruffly/wavy appearance. Fronds emerge light green but mature to deep green. Semi-evergreen in warm winter climates,
right	*Rhododendron* 'Elizabeth Ostbo'	3 ft. Red – blooms in **late April.**

❧ VISTA POINT - Area from Fern Bed, around the point, to the European White Birch.

GARDEN NOTES

Plants are listed from Left to Right. Improvements to this picnic and viewing area are ongoing.

	COMMON & BOTANICAL NAME	NOTES
left	American Sweet Gum *Liquidambar styracifula*	Beautiful red to purple fall color; same family as Ironwood tree. Native to SE US; used widely as street tree but gets ice-damage.
behind fence	Domestic Apple Tree *Malus cv.*	Part of Henry's old orchard, on "wild side" of fence.
left	European Cranberry Bush *Viburnum trilobum*	Deciduous, showy red berries in fall and winter.
center	Convex Japanese Holly *Ilex crenata* 'Convexa'	Evergreen to 5'; female clone; Hollies are dioecious (have male and female flowers on separate plants.)
right	Rose *Rosa* 'Sally Holmes' & "Carefree Delight'	
right	Japanese Maple *Acer palmatum* variety	
right	Rose *Rosa* 'Dublin Bay' & 'Color Magic'	

🎋 BRISTLECONE PINE BED - Along inside of wslk between the Weeping Cherry tree and the Rhododendrons.

GARDEN NOTES

	COMMON & BOTANICAL NAME	NOTES
	Weeping Flowering Cherry *Prunus pendula* 'Pendula Rosea'	Pink flowers in spring; in rose family and suseptible to same diseases—sometimes badly defoliated by leaf spots and brown rot.
	Globe Blue Spruce *Picea pungens* (Glauca Group) 'Globosa'	Slow growing dwarf form; next to Bristlecone Pine.
	Bristlecone Pine *Pinus aristata*	Small twisted pine; oldest tree in the world—lives to be 10,000 years old in Sierra Nevada Mountains. Scales are normal & caused by pitch exudates.
behind globe spruce	Rheingold Golden *Arborvitae Thuja occidentalis* 'Rheingold'	Dwarf, globe shaped grows 3-6"/yr to 3-6 ft in 10 yrs. Bright yellow orange in spring/summer w/interior lime green foliage; copper/orange tint in winter.
behind bristle cone	Dwarf Norway Nest Spruce *Picea abies* 'Elegans'	Low, rounded specimen grows 3-6"/yr to 3-6 ft wide in 10 years. New growth in spring is bright light green..
top	Oriental Spruce *Picea orientalis* 'Gowdy'	Narrow column, dark green shiny needles. Branches hang out and down, creating a weeping effect. To 12-15ft tall x 6-8 ft wide in 10 years.
top	Dwarf Lodgepole Pine *Pinus contortia* 'Chief Joseph'	Dwarf pine grows 4"/yr to 8-12'x4-5' in 10 yrs. Light green foliage turns yellow/gold in winter. Discovered in Eastern OR.
top	Prostrate Blue Deodar Cedar *Cedrus deodara* 'Prostrate Beauty'	Low spreading cedar, 6-12"/yr to 6' in 10 yrs. Blue color w/feathery texture.
mid right	Snow Sprite Dwarf Deodar Cedar *Cedrus deodara* 'Snow Sprite	Upright, broad, dwarf cedar grows 6-12"/yr to 5-7' in 10yrs. Bright creamy white foliage.
mid	Cole's Prostrate Canadien Hemlock *Tsuga canadensis* 'Cole's Prostrate'	Slow growing flat spreading Hemlock. Grows 3-6"/yr.
mid left	Mops Mugo Pine *Pinus mugo* 'Mops'	Dwarf pine forms a low, dense dome. Grows 2"-3"/yr reaching 2'-3 ft in 10 yrs. Green w/grey-blue tinges most of the year but w/golden hue in cold winter months.

		COMMON & BOTANICAL NAME	NOTES
mid		Paper Bark Maple *Acer griseum*	Chinese species with 3-parted leaves and beautiful, peeling cinnamon bark.
left		*Rhododendron degronianum ssp. yakushimanum* 'Yaku Angel'	Semi-dwarf, compact. Leaves have a fawn colored indumentums on the underside. Pink buds open to pure white flowers in **April**.
bottom		Pacific Coast Iris hyb mix	'Drive You Wild' (mauve/red), 'Native Warrior'(mauve/maroon /wt edges) & 'Canyon Snow' (wt/yellow patch)
bottom		Iris *Iris sibirica*	Henry Pittock's favorite flower.
left		Mollis Azalea *Rhododendron japonicum x R. molle*	Deciduous; yellow and red flowers in **April/May**. No fragrance (Exburys have fragrance).
left end		Unique Rhododendron *Rhododendron* 'Album Elegans'	Pink buds, pale yellow to white blooms in **May**.
		Red Oak *Quercus rubra*	Large tree above rhododendron. Named for its reddish wood color; seeds itself about.

❧ SKY BORDER - Along the outside of the Point Walk, from the bench under the European White Birch to the Gate Lodge.

GARDEN NOTES

Originally a narrow Rose-only border, it was expanded to include perennial in 2008 & 2009. The design is to create a color scheme representing the colors of the sky from dawn (East), to Mid-day (Center), to dusk (West). There are over 100 separate varieties of roses and perennials in this bed.

Plants are listed in approximately 15' sections, from left (dawn) to right (dusk) and from back to front.

	COMMON & BOTANICAL NAME	NOTES
TREE	European White Birch *Betula pendula*	Tree. Largest specimen in Portland; 80—100 years old!
	DAWN/SUNRISE SECTION	Vibrant sky colors: purples, golds, oranges, reds, pinks.
back	Rose *Rosa 'Artistry' (Hybrid Tea)*	Orange-pink, double form
back	Upright Clematis *Clematis recta* 'Midnight Mascarade'	Non-climbing clematis, dense clumps of metallic dark plum-purple foliage turning purple green in summer. Small white flowers **July-September.**
back	Foxglove *Digitalis purpurea* 'Foxy'	Long spikes shades of carmine-red, pink, creamy-yellow, white on 2' stalks, **spring/summer.** Numerous varieties of this plant throughout – it seeds itself about
back	*Rosa* 'Color Magic' (Hybrid Tea)	From ivory to drk rose-pink depending on amount of sun. 25-30 petals per bloom
back	Iris, cvs	Repeated along the fence throughout the first half of this bed.
mid	Bugbane *Actaea simplex* 'Black Negligee'	Purple tinted white fragrant flowers on dark 4 ft stems with lacy black foliage. **Summer** bloom. (Old name: *Cimicifuga*.)
mid	Golden Ray *Ligularia dentate* 'Othello'	Large blue-green velvet-fuzzy foliage w/burgundy colored stems and under leaf. Gold daisy-like flowers in **mid-summer.**
front	Heuchera *Heuchera* 'Obsidian'	Smooth ebony-maroon, rounded, lobed leaves w/long petioles. Small creamy flowers on 2' red-tinted stems in **June-July.**
front	Masterwort *Astrantia* 'Hadspen Blood'.	Bright green leaves w/red highlights & rose-red flowers in **spring**; reblooms in summer. 24"
front ? died?	Butterfly Gaura *Gaura lindheimeri*	Loose sprays of sm white, 5-petaled flowers tinged w/ pink on deep green foliage to 3-4 ft. Blooms **early summer to mid fall.**

	COMMON & BOTANICAL NAME	NOTES
front	Day Lily *Hemerocallis* 'Final Touch'	Large 5", fragrant soft lavender-pink flower with green throat on 30" stems. **Late summer** bloom. Repeated in mid and sunset end of this bed.
back	*Rosa* 'Double Knockout' (Modern shrub rose)	Medium red w/18-25 petals per bloom (shorter than advertized – will need to be moved).
back	*Rosa* 'Morning Magic' (Climber)	Light pink – single form w/8 petals per bloom.
back	Tall Verbena *Verbena bonariensis*	Slender, willowy stems stand to 6 ft tall and do not need staking. It branches widely near top in **late summer** w/rich lilac-purple flower clusters. Spreads.
back	Summer Phlox *Phlox paniculata* 'Nicky'	Giant deep bright purple flowering panicle clusters on 3' to 4' stems w/mid-green foliage. **June-Sept.**
mid	*Rosa* 'Flower Girl' (Modern shrub)	Light pink – single form.
mid	Rose *Rosa* 'Watercolors' (Modern shrub)	Colors change daily: yellow, pink, cerise, ruby tones. Single blooms in clusters. Repeated again before Lamp Post.
mid	*Ligularia przewalskii* 'Dragon's Wings'	Green, deeply dissected, palmate foliage with 5' upright-spikes of golden yellow flowers on purplish-black stems in the **summer.**
front	*Rosa* 'Pink Drift' (Ground cover)	Deep pink w/8 petals per bloom. Repeated twice after Chestnut tree.
front	Beard Tongue *Penstemon x mexicale* 'Sunburst Ruby'	White centered, ruby-red tubular flowers on 15" stems above bushy foliage. Blooms **June-August.**
Front	Black-eyed Susan *Rudbeckia fulgida* 'Goldstrum'	2-3' x 2-3'. Golden daisies with brown central cones.
back	Daffodil *Narcissus*, cvs	Narrow, rush-like leaves w/yellow trumpet-centered blossoms. Die back after **spring** bloom. (Sm & Lg varieties repeated throughout bed)
back	Clematis *Clematis* 'Sapphire Indigo'™	Dark purple buds open to med-large deep purple-pink flower fading to deep blue. Dark purple stamen.
back	Purple Beautyberry *Callicarpa dichotoma* 'Early Amethyst'	3-4 ft round bushy shrub w/arching branches. Small lavender-pink flowers at center of leaf in **summer.** Rose-purple foliage in fall & clusters of amethyst berries Sept-Nov on bare branches.
back	Foxglove *Digitalis purpurea* 'Camelot Rose'	Rose/mauve flowers w/spotted interior on 3-4' stalks above velvet/fuzzy textured foliage. Blooms **late spring – early summer.**
mid	*Rosa* 'Sun Flare' (Floribunda)	Bright lemon yellow, dbl form, 25-30 petals (to be moved to 'mid-day' in fall).
mid	Cone Flower *Echinacea pupurea* 'Hope'	Large soft light-pink reflex petals w/orange disks on 20"-30" stems. Blooms **mid-summer to fall**.
mid	*Rosa* 'Grace' (DA English)	Apricot, darker in middle, 41+ petals per bloom.

	COMMON & BOTANICAL NAME	NOTES
mid	*Rosa* 'Pink Knockout' (Modern shrub)	Medium pink – single form
mid	Hyssop *Agastache* 'Raspberry Summer'	Large tubular dark raspberry-pink flowers stand on dense spikes **Summer-Fall**. Leaves used for tea.
mid	Hummingbird Mint *Agastache* 'Summer Sky'	Low mound of drk green foliage bearing dark upright spikes of glowing violet-blue flowers **summer to fall**. Attracts both hummingbirds and butterflies.
mid	Beard Tongue *Penstemon barbatus* 'Elfin Mix'	Tall 12 to 18"spikes of warm pink tubular bell flowers w/ glossy evergreen foliage. **June – Sept.**
front	*Rosa* 'Coral Drift' (Ground cover)	Orange pink w/20+ petals per bloom. Repeated at sunset/ dusk end of bed.
front	Salvia (Sage) *Salvia nemorosa* 'Marcus'	Deep purple-blue flowers on 12" spikes above compact mounding grey-green foliage blooming **June – October.**
back	Gold Flame Honeysuckle Vine *Lonicera x hechrottii* 'Gold Flame'	Deciduous leaves are dark green on the surface and blue-green underneath. Fragrant flowers, pink on the outside and orange-yellow inside. Free flowering from **June to September**. The stems are slightly twining in habit. It can also be grown as a shrub. It attains the height of 3-6 m.
back	Iris cvs - repeat	
back	Clematis (viticella group) *Clematis* 'Venosa Violacea'	4-5" bicolor flower vivid violet w/white stripe center (star effect). Blooms **July & August.**
back	*Clematis* 'Betty Corning' (viticella group)	Bluish-purple bell-shaped blooms from **early summer – fall.**
mid	Black-eyed Susan *Rudbeckia subtomentosa* 'Henry Eilers'	Basal leaves appear in early spring, flowering stalks begin their ascent in June, reaching 5 to 6 feet and full flower by **August thru Sept**. Flowers have finely quilled petals of true yellow, not gold,
mid	Peony *Paeonia lactiflora x lemoine* 'Bartzella'	A 3 ft hybrid between tree and herbaceous peonies. Flowers are the color, size and form of the tree peonies without a trunk or branches. Fully double 9" bright yellow flowers w/hint of red at base when fully open. Can produce 80 blossoms in a **late spring/early summer**. Repeated in Mid-day section.
mid	*Rosa* 'Watercolors' - repeat	(To be moved in fall.)
mid	Beard Tongue *Penstemon barbatus* 'Elfin Pink'	Narrow, lance-shaped leaves. Long panicles of pendant, tubular, clear pink flowers from **early summer – early fall**.
mid	Beard Tongue *Penstemon heterophyllus*	Bright blue tubular flowers on 18" stems above mounding glossy deep green foliage w/red & bronze highlights. Blooms all **summer**.
front	*Rosa* 'Red Drift' (Ground cover)	Medium red w/15 petals per bloom

	COMMON & BOTANICAL NAME	NOTES
front	Beard Tongue *Penstemon* 'Dark Towers'	Glossy bronze-red foliage topped w/masses of pink tubular flowers in **July & August.**
front	*Rosa* ' Rainbow Sunblaze' (Min.)	Small blooms-bright yellow cast & red undertones. Repeated at end of bed.
	MID-DAY SECTION	Sky colors mainly blues, whites and yellows.
back	Iris cvs - repeat	
back	Asiatic Lily *Lilium Asiatic* Lily Hybrid cvs	Tall cream-yellow fragrant lily Repeated along fence throughout .
back	*Echinacea x* 'Flame Thrower'	40"x40" Rebloomer has two-toned orange and yellow flowers all summer.
mid	Peachleaf Bellflower *Campanula persicofolia* 'Telham Beauty'	3'x1.5' Large, nodding, sky-blue, bell-shaped flowers borne upright on slender, leafless spikes over a glossy green mound in late spring and summer.
mid	Bellflower *Campanula latiloba* 'Highcliffe'	Evergreen perennial with erect, leafy stems and bright-green leaves. Has short, spike-like, racemes of deep violet-blue, cup-shaped flowers in summer.
mid	*Rosa* 'Kew Gardens' (DA English)	
mid	*Rosa* 'High Voltage' (Modern Shrub)	Medium yellow, dbl form, 22 petals
front	Yarrow *Achillea* 'Appleblossom'	Pastel pink-peach flower clusters rising up to 36" above 6-9" ferny foliage from June - September
front	Peony 'Bartzella' - repeated	
front	LAMP POST	Just to give you your bearings!
front	Rocky Mountain Columbine *Aquilegia x caerulea* 'Origami Mix'	Lacy foliage w/blue & white 2" bloom with long spurs on slender, erect stems. Spring & early summer.
front	Dwarf Catmint *Nepeta racemosa* 'Little Titch'	Tightly packed gray-green leaves, in a low growing, dense mat. Adorning stem tips, small heads of rich blue flowers bloom all summer long.
back	*Rosa* ' Lunar Mist' (Climber)	Sm climber/lg shrub – white blend w/50+ petals Repeated
back	*Rosa* 'Darlow's Enigma' (Rambler)	White with golden centers – Semi-double form Repeated
mid - back	Butterflies Magnolia *Magnolia* 'Butterflies'	Pyramidal deciduous tree. 20-30ft tall, 12-15ft spread. 3-4-inch, fragrant, buttery lemon-yellow flowers with red stamens (resemble swarms of butterflies) appear in April before the tree leafs out. Repeated
back	Roses repeated	'Darlow's Enigma' and 'Lunar Mist'

	COMMON & BOTANICAL NAME	NOTES
mid	Shasta Daisy *Chrysanthemum*, cvs	3.5ft herbaceous, clump-forming perennial with dark green leaves. In summer to autumn it bears large, white, daisy-like flowers with yellow centres.
mid	*Geum* 'Gold Ball'	2'x2' golden yellow, semi-dbl flowers above clumps of drk green, pinnate leaves.
front	Blue Star Flower *Amsonia* 'Blue Ice'	Compact plant 12-15"x 24" w/blue, star-like flowers in **spring**. Foliage turns brilliant yellow in fall.
front	Catmint *Nepeta* 'Walker's Low'	24-30 inches tall. Loose whorls of many small, trumpet-shaped, lavender-blue flowers on aromatic, gray-green foliage. Blooms from **spring to fall** if sheared (deadheaded).
front	Tickseed *Coreopsis* 'Crème Brulee'	A spreading mound of bright-green ferny leaves with small butter-yellow daisies from **early summer to late fall**; each petal is delicately serrated at the tips. Shear plants lightly in August to encourage renewed blooming.
back	*Rosa* 'Spanish Sunset' (Floribunda)	Dark orange/yellow mix w/yellow center, pinks as they age, 10 petals (to be moved in fall)
back	*Rosa* 'Full Moon Rising' (Climber)	Cream yellow, ruffled edge blossoms.Repeated again in mid-day section of bed.
back	Tickseed *Coreopsis* 'Autumn Blush'	Soft yellow, maroon eyed daisy flower on 24" stem over low mounding ferny foliage. Yellow develops to peachy blush in fall. **Early summer to fall.** Repeated frequently.
back	*Clematis* 'Westerplatte' cv	4-6" velvet-red blooms w/deeper red anthers. Blooms **June – September.**
mid	Bellflower *Campanula punctala* 'Plum Wine'	Dark wine colored serrated foliage w/elongated mauve flowers on 15" stems. **May-September.**
mid	Tickseed *Coreopsis* 'Full Moon'	30"x24" Dense mound of foliage with a multitude of large 3" canary yellow blooms **midsummer through fall.**
mid	Peach-leaf Bellflower *Campanula persicifola* 'Alba'	Upright 3 ft tall x 1 ft wide bright; green, lance-shaped leaves w/ large, racemose, white bell-shaped flowers. **Early summer.**
mid	Repeated *Hemerocallis* 'Final Touch'.	
mid	Tickseed *Coreopsis* 'Sunshine Superman'	Blooms non-stop from **mid-summer to October** with saucer-like golden yellow flowers over low spreading, slightly fuzzy foliage.
mid	White Sage, Wormwood *Artemesia* 'Valerie Finnis'	18" upright plant of large, soft, silvery-white leaves lobed near the tip. Dense yellowish-gray flower panicles in **August.** Repeated multiple times later in this bed.
front	*Rosa* 'Pink Drift' (Ground cover)	Deep pink w/8 petals per bloom. Repeated later in this bed.
back	Tall Asiatic Lily, *Coreopsis* 'Autumn Blush', Artemesia 'Valerie Finnis',	Repeated back and mid in this section.

	COMMON & BOTANICAL NAME	NOTES
back	*Rosa* 'Scepter'd Isle' (DA English)	Light pink w/45 petals per bloom
back	Dwarf Lupine *Lupinus polyphyllus* 'Gallery Red'	18-24". Distinctive palmate leaves with dense spikes of sweetpea-shaped flowers, **late spring/early summer.**
back	Clematis 'Haku Ookan' (florida group)	Purple blooms; single, semi-double & double on same plant.
mid	Summer Phlox *Phlox paniculata* 'David'	Giant white flowering panicle clusters on 2-4' stems w/ mid-green foliage. **Summer to early fall**.
mid	Blue Anise Sage *Salvia guaranitica* 'Black & Blue'	6 ft tall, semi-woody perennial subshrub with a loose, bushy, open form. Has 2" deep blue, tubular flowers with dark purple calyces on 10" spikes from **early summer to late fall**. The flowers have hoodlike upper lip and a shorter, downward pointing lower lip.
mid	Dwarf Lupine *Lupinus* 'The Governor'	Dense spikes of deep violet-blue, pea-shaped flowers above clusters of fan-shaped, divided leaves on long leafstalks
mid	*Rosa* 'Happy Child' (DA English)	3'x3' Deep yellow 4" dbl, cup-shaped.
mid	*Coreopsis* 'Autumn Blush'	Repeated frequently.
mid	White Sage, Wormwood *Artemesia* 'Valerie Finnis'	Repeated frequently
front	Hardy Geranium *Geranium x* 'Brookside'	Sapphire-blue blooms in **early summer & fall** w/ dark green foliage turning intense shades of red and golden-orange in autumn. Repeated later in this bed
front	*Rosa* 'Peach Drift' (Ground cover)	Pink blend w/15-20 petals per bloom. Repeated later.
back	Blue Mist Spirea *Caryopteris clandonensis* 'Dark Knight'	3-4' x 4' deciduous shrub. Tidy, upright growth habit and profusion of long-blooming, deep blue flowering spikes **mid-late summer to fall**. Prune back hard in early spring – blooms on new growth.
back	Rose (David Austen English) *Rosa* 'Crown Princess Margareta'	Apricot/apricot blend w/120 petals per bloom.
back	Rose Unidentified Climber	Pink and white. Repeated numerous times along the fence in this bed.
back	*Rosa* 'Crocus Rose' (DA English)	Apricot/apricot blend w/110 petals per bloom
mid & front	Artemisia; Coreopsis; Rosa 'Rainbow Sunblaze', 'Peach Drift', and 'Pink Drift'; daffodil, Echinacea, and Bartzella Peony.	Repeated mid and front in this section.
mid	Yarrow *Achillea* 'Moonshine'	Canary yellow, wide flat-heads rising 30" ABOVE 6-9" gray-green feathery foliage, **June – Sept**.

	COMMON & BOTANICAL NAME	NOTES
mid	Anise Hyssop, Licorice Mint *Agastache* 'Golden Jubilee'	Sma;; bluish-purple flowers top 20" spikes over an upright compact clump of foliage, golden to chartreuse at top, lime green toward bottom; long-lasting blooms slowly increase in length in weeks to follow. Will bloom **June-Oct** if dead-headed.
mid	*Rosa* 'Easy Does It' (Floribunda)	Orange-pink, large scalloped bloom, 26-40 petals.
back, mid & front	Asiatic lily; 'Crown Princess Margareta', 'Full Moon Rising', unk climber roses; Coreopsis var; Geranium, daffodil, and Artemesia	Repeated back. mid and front.
back	*Rosa* 'Benjamin Britten' (DA Eng)	Orange-red w/60 petals per bloom.
mid & front	*Ligularia przewalskii* 'Dragon's Breath'	Golden yellow flowers appear in **June** on purple black stems above the deep green cut-leaf foliage. Needs a moist location 13x22" w/flower spikes to 2.5 ft.
mid	Tickseed *Coreopsis* 'Full Moon'	30"x24" Dense mound of foliage with a multitude of large 3" canary yellow blooms **midsummer through fall.**
mid	*Rosa* 'Pascali' (Hybrid Tea)	Creamy white, dbl form, 30-35 petals.
mid	*Rosa* 'Seafoam' (mod shrub)	White
mid	Beard Tongue 'Electric Blue' *Penstemon heterophyllus*	Bright blue tubular flowers on 18" stems above mounding glossy deep green foliage w/red & bronze highlights. Blooms **all summer.**
mid	Pincushion Flower *Scabiosa caucasia* 'House's Hybrids'	Blue to lavender 'pincushion' flowers on 18-24" stems over mound of deeply cut foliage. Blooms **early to mid summer.**
front	Pincushion Flower *Scabiosa columbaria* 'Butterfly Blue'	Many sky blue to blue purple 'pincushion' flowers on 15" stems over compact ferny blue-green foliage. Blooms **May to October.**
mid	Hyssop *Agastache x* 'Blue Fortune'	2-3'x2-3' Strong 3' stems have fuzzy, licorice-scented leaves topped with hundreds of large blue-lavender bottlebrush flowers **early spring thru summer.** Attract pollinators.
mid	Goldleaf Blue Mist Spirea *Caryopteris clandonensis* 'Worchester Gold'	Mounding, woody shrub with warm yellow to chartreuse foliage and lavender-blue flowers in **late summer and early autumn.**
mid	North African Sage *Salvia barrelieri*	Compact bluish green basal rosettes. Flower stalks branch & tower to 6 ft w/striking lavender-blue flowers from **June to fall**, opening from bottom to top, like delphiniums. At 2-3 ft use loop of jute to stabilize, do not stake!!

	COMMON & BOTANICAL NAME	NOTES
mid - back	Butterflies Magnolia *Magnolia* 'Butterflies'	Pyramidal deciduous tree. 20-30ft tall, 12-15 ft spread. 3-4", fragrant, buttery lemon-yellow flowers with red stamens (resemble swarms of butterflies) appear in **April** before the tree leafs out. Repeated
mid	Foxglove *Digitalis purpurea* 'Candy Mountain'	Rosy-pink/mauve bells w/freckled interior on 20" stalks above lance shaped rosette foliage. Blooms **late spring - early summer.**
mid	Foxglove *Digitalis purpurea* 'Lily's Lilac'	Warm lilac flowers w/deep purple-red interior on 2.5' stalks. Blooms **April – June.**
mid	Yarrow *Achillea* 'Appleblossom'	Pastel pink-peach flower clusters rising up to 36" above 6-9" ferny foliage from **June - September.**
front	*Rosa* 'Peach Drift	Repeat
	DUSK/SUNSET SECTION	
back	Clematis (viticella group) *Clematis* 'Ernest Markham'	Deep purple-magenta blooms fading to purplish-pink. **Mid-summer** to sporadic in **late summer**
back	*Clematis* 'Multi Blue' cv	Large deep blue double flowers – pom-poms remain long after petals fall.
back	Foxglove *Digitalis purpurea* 'Foxy'	Long spikes shades of carmine-red, pink, creamy-yellow, white on 2' stalks, **spring/summer.** Numerous varieties of this plant throughout – it seeds itself about.
mid	*Rosa* 'Fairy Meidiland' (Modern shrub)	Pink blend w/8-15 petals per bloom.
mid	*Rosa* 'Winner's Circle' (Climber)	Red blend w/8 petals per bloom.
mid	*Rosa* ' Sundance' (Hybrid Tea)	Large deep gold edged in pink-orange, 17-25 petals
mid	*Rosa* ' Lady of Shalott' (DA Eng)	Apricot-yellow, salmon-pink shading, golden-yellow reverse. Edges shaded pink. Strong, apple, clove, tea fragrance. 3" Medium, full, cluster-flowered, in small clusters.
mid	Hummingbird Mint *Agastache* 'Summer Sky'	Low mound of drk green foliage bearing dark upright spikes of glowing violet-blue flowers **summer to fall.** Attracts both hummingbirds and butterflies.
front	*Rosa* 'Coral Drift' (Ground cover)	Orange pink w/20+ petals per bloom.
front	Blue-eyed Grass *Sisyrinchium bellum*	A 1-foot tall perennial evergreen grass with 1 inch blue flowers in Jan.-June. It has small, iris-like leaves.
back	Foxglove *Digitalis purpurea* 'Glittering Prizes'	Large mottled purple, lilac, cream, white, rose, w/purple blotched interior on 6' stalks. Blooms late spring - early summer.

	COMMON & BOTANICAL NAME	NOTES
back	Foxglove *Digitalis purpurea* 'Foxy'	Long spikes shades of carmine-red, pink, creamy-yellow, white on 2' stalks, **spring/summer**. Numerous varieties of this plant throughout – it seeds itself about
back	Joe Pye Weed *Eupatorium dubium* 'Baby Joe'	24-30" Masses of lavender-rose flowers bloom in large, domed, flower heads over bright green foliage throughout **summer**.
back & mid	Garden Sage *Salvia nemorosa* 'May Night'	Compact, clump forming plant of aromatic, oblong leaves and long spikey violet-blue flowers on 18" purple-red stems. Will bloom all **summer into the fall** if deadheaded.
	Asiatic Lily, daffodil, Foxglove var., and 'Morning Magic' rose	Plants repeated in this section.
back	Mountain Meadow Rue *Thalictrum fendleri*	Squared small leaflets held along compound leaves on stems to 6 ft., capped in **early summer** by a froth of greenish-yellow flowers. (full sun)
back	Dwarf Meadow Rue *Thalictrum kuisianum* (at base of T.fendleri)	An erect clump-forming perennial 6"-10". Dainty purplish blue-green leaves with heads of pink or purple flowers **June-August. Note:** These two Meadow Rue show a good example of the range in size, leaf, and flower of this plant with over 200 varieties.)
back	Meadow Rue *Thalictrum aquilegiifolium* 'Black Stockings' LEAVES LOOK LIKE COLUMBINE.	Fluffy lavender-pink flowers in large flat-topped corymbs on nearly black 4'-5'stems in **late spring, early summer**. Foliage forms a loose mound of light green 48"x24". Must be vernalized (subject to low temperatures) to bloom.
back	Upright Clematis *Clematis recta* 'Midnight Mascarade'	Non-climbing clematis, dense clumps of metallic dark plum-purple foliage turning purple green **in summer**. Small white flowers July-September.
back	*Rosa* 'Huntington' (DA English)	Deep pink w/100 petals per bloom.
mid	Sneezeweed *Helenium* 'Sahin's Early Flowerer'	3'x2' flowers open deep red with a brown and yellow central cone, then develop orange and yellow streaks on the petals.
mid	*Rosa* 'Topsy Turvy' (Floribunda)	Red blend w/10-15 petals per bloom.
mid	Weigelia *Weigelia florida* 'Dark Horse'	24-36" compact deciduous shrub. Dark bronze leaves with striking lime-green venation and magenta-pink flowers **late spring/early summer.**
mid	Masterwort *Astrantia* 'Hadspen Blood'.	Bright green leaves w/red highlights & rose-red flowers in **spring**; reblooms in **summer**. 24"
mid	Cushion Spurge *Euphorbia* 'Blackbird'	Velvety foliage that darkens to near black in full sun. Flowers open above bright, lime green bracts on red stems that form a compact vase shape.
front	*Rosa* 'Wing Ding' (Modern shrub)	Scarlet 8 petal blooms in pyramid-shape clusters.
front	*Rosa* ' Rainbow Sunblaze' (Min.)	Sm blooms-bright yellow cast & red undertones.

	COMMON & BOTANICAL NAME	NOTES
under maple	Coral Bells *Heuchera cvs*	'Chocolate Ruffles', 'Fantasia', 'Midnight Rose', 'Milan', 'Mint Frost', 'Obsidian', 'Plum Royale', and 'Starry Nights'.
TREE	Japanese Maple, cvs	
	CUT FLOWER BED	A 2010 Project.
back	*Rosa* 'Queen Elizabeth' (Floribunda)	Medium pink, double form.
back	*Rosa* 'About Face' (Floribunda)	4' to 6' Orange blend (under-petal bronzy, upper golden yellow.) Mild, apple fragrance. 30 to 35 petals. Avg dia 4". Borne mostly solitary, old-fashioned bloom form.
back	Clematis (jackmanii group) *Clematis* 'Niobe'	Buds open to nearly black & mature to dark ruby red w/ gold anthers on 12' vine. **June – Sept.**
back	Magnolia Vine *Schisandra chinensis* 'Apricot Blush'	A monoecious plant (separate male & female flowers on same plant) small creamy white/pink blossoms **May-June.** Scarlet berries in grape-like clusters mid-August – Sept.
back & front	*Rosa* 'Beverly' (Kordes Hybrid Tea)	32" Pink blend. Strong, citrus fragrance. 45+ petals. Avg dia 3.5". Solitary, high-centered bloom form.
mid	Ligularia *Ligularia stenocuphala*	Large, long stalked, kidney-shaped leaves with **mid to late summer** spikes of bright yellow flowers on purple stems up to 5ft tall.
mid	Baneberry (Autopurpurea Group) *Actaea simplex* 'Brunette'	3 ft plant with deep purple, deeply toothed foliage accented by pinkish-white bottle-bush blossoms in **fall** rising on stems to 5ft. Prefers part to full shade
mid	*Lobelia x* 'Queen Victoria'	Vertical plant to 3-4 ft. Dark, purple-red foliage with spikes of scarlet tubular flowers **in summer.**
mid	*Rosa* 'Artistry' (Hybrid Tea)	4' to 5' Orange-pink. Mild, sweet fragrance. 26 to 40 petals. Avg dia 5". Blooms throughout **season.** Pointed, ovoid buds.
front	*Rosa* 'Black Magic' (Hybrid Tea)	5.5' to 7' Dark red. None to mild, sweet fragrance. 30 to 40 petals. Avg dia 4.5". Large, high-centered bloom form. Pointed, ovoid buds.
front	*Rosa* 'Grande Dame' (Hybrid Tea)	5' Deep pink. Strong fragrance. 31+ petals.
front	*Rosa* 'Rouge Royale' (Hybrid Tea)	4'-5' Red. Strong, anise, raspberry, strawberry, sweet fragrance. 41+ petals, old-fashioned, quartered bloom form.
front	Globeflower Trollius 'Cheddar', 'Lemon Queen', and 'Pritchard's Giant'	Gracing gardens since the 16th century, these marvelous yellow-hued blooms inspired their name, which translates to "basin" in Latin or "globe" in German. Buttercup-like blossoms perch on straight stems above handsome, deeply divided glossy leaves throughout **summer.**

	COMMON & BOTANICAL NAME	NOTES
back	Bee Balm *Monarda didyma* 'Jacob Cline'	Enormous red frilly starburst blossoms perch atop tall square stems of highly fragrant foliage from June through August. Hummingbird magnet.
back	*Rosa* 'Heritage' (DA English shrub)	Light pink, dbl, cupped (Donated '09 by Wahkeena DAR to honor of Georgiana Pittock)
Back ??died	Voodoo Lily/Snake Plant *Amorphophallus konjac*	Exotic, aroid plant grown as a food crop in E. Asia. Has a snake skin pattern on stem.Once mature, produces a very large (measured in feet), deep burgundy, plastic looking spathe that stinks like rotted meat until pollination is complete.
mid & front	Peachleaf Bellflower *Campanula persicofolia*	Repeat.
front	*Rosa* 'Jean Giono' (Hybrid Tea)	Yellow blend w/100 petals per bloom.
front	Ornamental Rhubarb *Rheum Palmatum v. tanguticum* 'Rote Auslese'	Purple tinted 2-3 ft wide leaves w/tooth-edges growing to 6-8 ft tall & 6 ft wide. Flower plumes to 2 ft long.
	Vegetable Garden	Display – not all vegetables mature because of limited direct sunlight. Some plants from the Potager Garden are being "housed" here during the 2013 renovation of the Mansion's main terraces.

❧ MAPLE GROVE - Along inside of walk from large Rhododendrons to Colorado Blue Spruce.

GARDEN NOTES

This area will be under renovation in 2013 – some of the old groundcovers will be removed and replaced.

	COMMON & BOTANICAL NAME	NOTES
	Coral Bark Maple *Acer palmatum* 'Sango Kaku'	Coral colored bark on new twigs; color is lost on older stems; bright yellow fall color.
	Laceleaf Maple *Acer palmatum var. dissectum*	Drapes to the ground; will reach 15' wide and 10' tall if not pruned. Often pruned in a Bonsai fashion to accentuate the trunk and limb structure.
	Full Moon Maple *Acer japonicum*	Deciduous, deeply cut lobed leaves turn brilliant crimson in fall; to 30'.
	Fernleaf Full-Moon Maple *Acer japonicum* 'Aconitifolium'	Small 8-10 ft tree. Deeply cut leaves reminds one of an Aconite (Monkshood) glorious shades of crimson, orange, and red in autumn.
	Heath *Erica x darleyensis cv.*	Valuable evergreen; full sun and good drainage best; shear lightly after flowering. (at top of hill). **Winter** flowering.
	Neon Flash Spirea *Spiraea japonica* 'Neon Flash'	Yellowish new foliage; lime- green in **summer**; bright red fall color; pink 3" flowers in mid-Summer.
	Cotoneaster *Cotoneaster damerii*	Evergreen groundcover; Red berries in **summer-fall**; bees love white flowers.
	Heather *Calluna vulgaris cv.*	Evergreen; give light shearing after bloom; full sun and moist, well drained soil; heavy lavender colored **mid-summer** bloom
top of hill	Kousa (Korean) Dogwood *Cornus kousa*	Deciduous, cream white flowers in **May-June**. (Near walk at back end of Georgiana's East Bed)
	European Cranberry Bush *Viburnum trilobum* 'Compactum'	Deciduous, showy red berries in **fall and winter**; dwarf cultivar.
	Blue Spruce *Picea pungens* 'Glauca Group	Large blue Spruce.

GATE LODGE - On both sides of the entrance to the Gate Lodge.

GARDEN NOTES

This was the home of James Skene, groundskeeper, and family.

	COMMON & BOTANICAL NAME	NOTES
	Bleeding Heart *Dicentra* 'Luxurient'	Herbaceous perennial, fernlike foliage.by Gate Lodge; red flowers from **mid-spring to early summer**; 12" plant.
	Bishop's Hat *Epimedium x rubrum*	Perennial, shade groundcover, pink/red blooms, bronze leaves in **summer/fall**. Gate Lodge side; Barberry family.
	Susan Magnolia *Magnolia* 'Susan'	Purple flowers in **May** before the leaves emerge; one of the Little Girl hybrids from the National Arboretum.
	Fern	
	Lilac	
	Convex Japanese Holly *Ilex crenata* 'Convexa'	Evergreen to 5'; female clone; Hollies are dioecious (have male and female flowers on separate plants.)
on trellis	*Clematis* 'Nellie Moser'	Vine that can reach to12 ft long. Blooms from **late May through summer** with starburst shaped flowers 5-7 inches across with white ruffled edges and mauve or pink-colored petals
on trellis	*Rosa* 'Zephirine Drouhin'	Abundant loosely cupped and semi-double cerise pink blooms in clusters; repeats. Bred in 1868 in France; one of the most popular roses of all time. Almost thornless. Foliage begins as coppery-purple and then turns a rich, dark green. Climber to 8-12 ft.
	Hydrangea cv	Mophead type.
	Slender Hinoki False Cypress *Chamaecyparis obtusa* 'Gracilis'	Evergreen has a slender pyramidal habit with whorled, flattened sprays of dark green foliage and slightly drooping branch tips. 15 ft.
	Wild Ginger *Asarum caudatum*	Evergreen native groundcover; likes shade; showy part of hidden flowers actually the calyx.
	High Bush Blueberry *Vaccinium corymbosum*	Edible blue fruits; Heath family.
	Variegated Weigela *Weigela* "Florida Variegata'	Deciduous, funnel shaped pink flowers in **spring**.

	COMMON & BOTANICAL NAME	NOTES
	Elizabeth Magnolia *Magnolia* 'Elizabeth'	Butter cream flowers in **April** before the leaves.
	Spanish Chestnut *Castanea sativa*	Edible nuts full of carbohydrates.
Also: St John's Wort, Persicaria, tassel fern, lilac; Double File Viburnum, Yew (behind the fence).		

🌿 SKENE'S HILL & TROUGH GARDEN- The steep hill from the Gate Lodge to the back of the Mansion, bordered by the stairs and the walk to the service terrace. Includes the Troughs in the alcove at the base of the stairs, in front of the Gate Lodge.

GARDEN NOTES

For many years, this hill area was entirely covered with invasive English Ivy and other aggressive ground covers. In 2010, the area was cleared, and since then, almost all new plantings have been 'harvested' from divisions of perennials such as Fern, Hosta, Heuchera, Astilbe, Pulmonaria, Sarcococca etc., located in other areas throughout the grounds – those plants are not listed with a description below.

Plants in the Trough Garden are identified by signs.

	COMMON & BOTANICAL NAME	NOTES
bottom	Snowmound Spirea *Spiraea nipponica* 'Snowmound'	Deciduous shrub, white blooms in **spring/summer**.
bottom	Mock Orange *Philadelphus lewisii*	Deciduous shrub, white blooms in **spring/summer**.
bottom	Sensation Lilac *Syringa vulgaris* 'Sensation'	Bi-colored violet rimmed-white flowers in **May; flowers revert to violet as plant ages.**
bottom	Bear's Breeches *Acanthus spinosus*	2'x3' evergreen perennial; showy large, deeply lobed, glossy green leaves with spiny tips. Pink or purple flowers on 2-3' spikes in **June & July**.
bottom	Variegated Bear's Breeches *Acanthus* 'Whitewater'	Deeply lobed and cut foliage that is heavily splashed with white. Will form a clump 3'wide, with 4'-tall pink & cream flower spikes in **June & July.**
bottom	*Hydrangea macrophyllia, cvs*	
bottom left	*Lungwort Pulmonaria –' Silver Bouquet'*	7x20", spotted leaves, mix of coral-pink, magenta, violet flower clusters in **spring** – this variety is sun tolerant.
middle left	Seven Sons Flower Tree *Heptacodium miconioides*	15-20ft tree/shrub with heart-shaped, deeply veined leaves. Large clusters of fragrant, creamy-white flowers at branch ends in **late summer & fall**, followed by masses of small fruits with bright purplish-red calyxes. Winter interest: thin, pale-tan strips peel away to reveal dark brown bark.
corner of wall	Prostrata Redwood *Sequoia sempervirens* 'Prostrata'	Low, slow-growing conifer with flat, gray-green needles and a wide, spreading habit. Growth to 2 ft tall & 8 ft wide.
top along walk	False Solomon's Seal *Smilacina racemosa*	Rhizomatous native to 3'; panicles of small white flowers in **spring**.

	COMMON & BOTANICAL NAME	NOTES
	Pacific Iris Hybrid *Iris douglasiana*	A 1 ft perennial with rhizomes that spread slowly into a 2 to 4 ft wide clump. Violet flowers arise in **spring** on a 1 to 2 ft high stem and three inches wide.
stairs near terrace	Spotted Dead Nettle *Lamium maculatum* 'Golden Anniversary'	8"x8" tight mound of dark green leaves w/ golden yellow edges and a white central stripe. Lavender flowers from **May to July.**
top near terrace	Japanese Maple *Acer palmatum* 'Shojo Nomura'	An upright deciduous tree with dark purple-red leaves. Fall color is fiery orange-red. The Japanese name means "beautiful red-faced monkey." (Color of summer foliage may be affected by the amount of sun-light.)
top near terrace	Fernleaf Full-moon Maple *Acer japonicum* 'Aconititolium'	Bright green, deep cut, fern-like leaves, which turn bright orange and red before falling.
top near terrace	Deadnettle, Yellow Archangel *Lamium galeobdolon* 'Herman's Pride' (under lace-leaf maple)	Clump forming groundcover to 1'x3'. Silvery, serrated-edged leaves with pronounced green veins. Masses of small bright, yellow-lipped flowers in **late spring to early summer.** Not as aggressive as some Lamium.
top near terrace	Glossy Abelia *Abelia x grandiflora*	Semi-evergreen; fragrant tubular bell shaped blooms in **summer/fall.** Related to Honeysuckle. On right, past the terrace.

Also along walk: Pieris, Mahonia (Oregon Grape), Ferns, Hosta, Comfry, Epimedium, Japanese Maples (around the service terrace).

	TROUGH GARDEN	Plants are identified by signage.
		The troughs in this area are from the Berry Botanical Garden, which closed in 2010. Also, in the Rock Garden and Woodland Areas are specimens from the BBG and the Jane Kerr Platt private garden. Georgiana Pittock (1846-1918) began a rich horticultural history in Portland, influencing the women who followed: Rae Selling Berry (1881-1976), and Jane Kerr Platt (1908-1989) were two of those Portland area women who became famous among horticulturists; we are honored to have plants from their gardens here.

🏵 **ROCK GARDEN**- The Rock Garden is across the drive from the front of the Gate Lodge and to the west of the stairway.

GARDEN NOTES

Renovation of this area started in late 2009, with clearing the area long over-run by hypericum and heather, and removing some plants not suitable for a rock garden; it continues with thinning sedum and adding and experimenting with new plants. (Many old existing plants remain to be identified, but ID signs will be in place for many of the new plants.)

Plants in this bed grow much more slowly and mostly require a more gritty, less fertile, and more well drained soil than the other perennial beds on the grounds. We are lucky that the three sections of this bed have different sun exposure: Full Sun, Part Sun/Shade, and Shade; allowing for a larger variety of plants.

	COMMON & BOTANICAL NAME	NOTES
	EAST SECTION	From stair end to Montgomery Spruce; full sun.
above wall	Harlequin Glorybower *Clerodendrum trichotomum*	Tree. White flowers in **late summer**, blue fruit in Fall, crushed leaves smell like peanut butter! Will sucker from roots.
along wall edge	Weeping Hemlock *Tsuga canadensis* 'Cole's Prostrate'	Soft green ½" needles in a spiral arrangement on slender stems contrasting w/whitish gnarled bark. Grows slowly, 1.5ftx3ft in 10 yrs, spreading flat on the ground or cascading over walls.
at wall corner	Laceleaf Maple *Acer palmatum var. dissectum*	Drapes to the ground; will reach 15' wide and 10' tall if not pruned. Often pruned in a Bonsai fashion to accentuate the trunk and limb structure.
east end	Weeping Norway Spruce *Picea abies* 'Pendula'	¾-inch needles, deep green, very stiff and closely set on pendulous branches. Grows in a spreading fashion across the garden floor, no more than 3 feet off the ground, sprawling to 10ft often cascading over walls or other barriers.
east above	Bowbells Rhododendron *Rhododendron* 'Bowbells'	Deep pink buds open to light pink blooms in **spring**. Slow growing mounded form to 3' high. Exciting bronzy-copper new growth. Evergreen.
east above	*Spirea, cvs*	Spiraea shrubs are a tried and true garden shrub that has been used for over 300 years. Native to the Northern Hemisphere, there are over 70 species and some species have several dozen varieties.
east above	Creeping St. Johnswort *Hypericum calycinum*	Dense groundcover w/short-stalked opposing leaves on 1' stems & bright yellow 3" blooms throughout **summer**. Competes well with tree roots & controls erosion but is quite invasive. (Note: most removed in fall 2009.)

	COMMON & BOTANICAL NAME	NOTES
east above	Boulevard (Blue Moss) Cypress	Needled evergreen This false cypress cultivar is a dense pyramidal semi-dwarf evergreen shrub that features soft, silvery blue-gray foliage. It is slow growing, typically reaching 5-6' tall in 10 years.
east above	Whipcord Hebe *Hebe ochracea* 'James Stirling'	Golden, evergreen foliage and white flowers that emerge from stem tips in early **summer**. Forms an attractive shrub 12-18" high and wide that resembles a conifer.
east above & high	Pasque Flower *Pulsatilla vulgaris*	Deciduous. Finely cut leaves to 10" high. Large purple flowers in **spring**; ornamental seed heads. Full to part sun, very well drained, infertile soil.
east high & mid	Pasque Flower *Pulsatilla vulgaris* 'Papageno'	Low tufts or mound of ferny green leaves, bearing crocus-like flowers in **early spring** with single to double fringed petals, from white to soft pastel pinks, through to rich deep purple and red.
east high & mid	Miniature Alberta Spruce *Picea glauca* 'Pixie'	An upright narrow conical plant. Needles are dark-green and smaller than species, grows to 1 ft x 8" in 10 yrs. First introduced from Vancouver, BC Canada.
east high & mid	Dwarf Spruce *Picea glauca* 'Echiniformis'	Blue-grey dwarf spruce, globe shaped, slow growing. 8" high x 1 ft wide in 10 years.
east high	Dwarf Siberian Spruce *Picea omorika* 'Pimoko'	Showy, dark green needles accented with a bluish cast and silvery undersides. Reddish brown buds. Globe-shaped when young, develops multiple leaders and an upright, broad shape with maturity. 3-5 ft in 10 yrs (some sites say 1 ft in 10 yrs).
east end mid	Juniper leaf Thyme *Thymus neiceffii aff*	Carpeting thyme resembles a miniature creeping juniper, with narrow, scale-like leaves packed along the stem. Stems radiate out along the ground in a star-like pattern. 1"x16" Gray-green foliage and medium pink flowers in **early spring**.
east end mid	Lewisia *Lewisia cotyledon Hyb* 'Kanab'	
east end mid	Sisikiyou Lewisia *Lewisia cotyledon Hyb* 'Alba'	Evergreen succulent rosettes with pure white flowers. 10" X 12". Grow in sun to part shade, in gritty, well-drained soil, topdress with grit.
east middle	Stonecrop *Sedum* 'Chocolate Drop'	Lightly scalloped, dark chocolate-brown leaves with soft rose-colored flowers to 10" tall.
east middle	Sisikiyou Lewisia *Lewisia cotyledon Hyb* 'Rainbow'	Evergreen succulent rosettes with showy flowers - best cultivar for repeat blooming **throughout the season**. Deadhead for continued flowering. 10" X 12" Grow in sun to part shade, in gritty, well-drained soil, topdress with grit.
east middle	Columbian Bitteroot (Lewisia) *Lewisia columbiana var columbiana*	Evergreen rosettes of narrow linear leaves with clusters of pink flowers in **spring** to 6" high Sun to part shade, gritty soil.

	COMMON & BOTANICAL NAME	NOTES
east middle	Red Edge Hebe *Hebe albicans* 'Red Edge'	18"x24"Compact evergreen shrub with tightly arranged grey-green, red-rimmed ovate leaves; spikes of lilac flowers fade to white in **summer**. Sun to part shade in well drained poor to moderately fertile soil.
east end low & thru-out	White Diamond Sedum *Sedum pachyclados*	Tight, powder blue, glaucous evergreen foliage on short, spreading stems. 2" tall; non-invasive. Many light pink star flowers in **summer**.Requires sun to part shade, dryish soils with good drainage, esp in wet winters. Good crevice plant and edger.
east low	Sisikiyou Lewisia *Lewisia cotyledon Hyb* 'Sunset Strain'	Evergreen succulent rosettes with showy bold colored flowers. 10" X 12" Grow in sun to part shade, in gritty, well-drained soil, topdress with grit.
east low	Miniature Hinoki False Cypress *Chamaecyparis obtusa* 'Hage'	Dwarf, spherical and dark green. Some brown coloration in cold seasons. Blunt, paired leaves with 'X' markings underneath. Full sun. moist soil in cooler climate. 1ftx1. ft/10 yrs.
east low	False Autumn Crocus *Colchicum autumnale*	Large, broad leaves in spring and early summer which die back before flowering in **fall**.
east low	Short Pink *Dianthus subacaulis*	Small, lacy cushion with deep pink flowers in **summer**. 2" x 8-12" Sun to part shade in sharply drained soil with grit mulch
low & thru-out	Bugleweed *Ajuga reptans cv.*	Groundcover with purple-green foliage, upright blue flowers, sends out runners.
east above	Stonecrop *Sedum* 'Autum Joy'	Classic Sedum. 2-foot-tall stems carry gray-green fleshy leaves topped in **late summer** with green broccoli-like heads of flower buds that open pink and turn rusty red by fall.
east above	Mountain Laurel *Kalmia latifolia*	Relative of rhododendron but will take more sun; angular, bowl shaped flowers, East coast native.
east high	Weeping Hemlock *Tsuga canadensis* 'Cole's Prostrate'	Soft green ½" needles in a spiral arrangement on slender stems contrasting w/whitish gnarled bark. Grows slowly, 1.5 ftx3 ft in 10 yrs, spreading flat on the ground or cascading over walls.
east high	Pyrenean Saxifrage *Saxifraga x longifolia*	Silver leaved, encrusted rosettes, after several years produce a 24" panicle with dozens of cup-shaped white flowers. May form multiple or single rosettes. 2"x 8". Cool sun or part shade among rocks
east high above	Fendler Lip Fern *Cheilanthers fendleri*	(from BBG) Prefers northfacing slope w/some shade. Cheilanthes (lip ferns) is a genus of about 180 species of rock-dwelling ferns with a wide ranging distribution in warm, dry, rocky regions, often growing in small crevices high up on cliffs. Most are small, sturdy and evergreen. The leaves spring upright directly from the rootstocks looking like a minature stand of evergreen trees.

	COMMON & BOTANICAL NAME	NOTES
east high above	*Cotula hispida*	Low matting perennial w/closely branched, prostrate stems, lined w/ dissected, silvery leaves resembling a small artemisias. 1/3" button-like, bright yellow flowers, on wiry stems in **summer**.
east high above	Ozothamnus 'Country Park Silver'	Forms a low mat of intensely silver foliage up to 3" x 24". Grow in full sun in gritty or sandy soil with regular water.
east high	*Saxifraga,*	
east high	Mountain Heather *Phyllodoce caerulea*	8"x12" evergreen shrub. Dark green, linear leaves; many pitcher-shaped pink flowers on short stems **late spring to summer.** Prefers part shade in moderately fertile, moist soil.
east high	Stonecrop *Sedum* possibly 'Class Act'	
east high	*Penstemon davidsonii var. menziesii*	Mat-forming evergreen with small, rounded leaves, rooting stems and large lavender to purple flowers **in summer.**
east high	Cape Blanco Stonecrop Sedum *spathulifolium* 'Cape Blanco'	NW native forms evergreen mats of gray-green to deep red rosettes. Yellow flowers **May-July.** Full sun to light shade, well drained soil, low water.
east high	Dwarf Clematis *Clematis integrifolia*	
east middle	Globe Daisy *Globularia meridionalis*	5"x12" evergreen perennial with spoon-shaped, glossy green leaves and showy spherical lavender blue flowers over many weeks in **spring**. Full to part sun in well-drained soil.
east middle	White-eyed Grass *Sisyrinchium idahoense* 'Album'	Sparkling white star-shaped flowers with yellow throats shine above 5" tall semi-evergreen, grassy foliage.
east middle	Sea thrift *Armeria maritima* 'Cotton Tail'	Tufted mounds spread to 1 ft; leaves are 6 in. long. White flowers in tight clusters atop 6–10 in. stalks in **spring**.
east middle	Pacific Iris Hybrid *Iris douglasiana*	A 1 ft perennial with rhizomes that spread slowly into a 2 to 4 ft wide clump. Violet flowers arise in **spring** on a 1-2 ft high stem.
east middle	Minature Alberta Spruce *Picea glauca* 'Pixie'	An upright narrow conical plant. Needles are dark-green and smaller than species, grows to 1 ft x 8" in 10 yrs. First introduced from Vancouver, BC Canada.
east middle	Hybrid Columbine *Aquilegia jonesii x saximontana*	4"x 6" Small mounds of ferny, glabrous foliage with summer bloom pale blue flowers with white tipped spurs. (?? Survival)

	COMMON & BOTANICAL NAME	NOTES
east low	Cobweb Hen & Chicks *Sempervivum arachnoideum* 'Spumanti'	Hardy Sempervivums are evergreen, mat-forming succulents organized in clusters of large rosettes (hens) and smaller offset rosettes (chicks). Hens sporadically produce flower stalks and these large rosettes die after flowering with the smaller chicks growing into the empty space left behind. Although some gardeners remove the flower stalks, if left in place they attract beneficial insect pollinators. This variety has heavy webbing on bubbly rosettes up to 2 1/2" and spikes of rose colored flowers.
east low	Snow in Summer *Cerastium tomentosum*	Light grey-green cushion of evergreen foliage to 8", covered with white flowers in **early summer**. Extremely xeric (low moisture) once established. Can be sheared or mowed after bloom to maintain dense habit the rest of the season.
east low	*Spirea, cvs*	Repeated.
	Also in this garden:	Low growing Sedum (at least five unidentified varieties of linear and broad leaf), Ajuga, Foxglove, Lychnis, Iris, and Columbine spread throughout the rock garden.
	MID SECTION	From Montgomery Spruce to Prostrate Nordman Fir; part sun/shade.
mid above	Montgomery Spruce *Picea pungens* 'Montgomery'	A small, dense mounded shrub-tree with intensely silver-blue needles. Grows to 10 ftx8 ft. (This tree was damaged when larger tree came down and broke off the leader)
mid above	*Rhododendron pemakoense*	Dwarf to 1 ft. Tubular, funnel-shaped, pink to pale purplish-mauve blossoms **early to mid-season**.
mid above	Blueberry & ?Huckleberry bushes	
mid above &thru out	Rose Campion *Lychnis coronaria*	An erect, many-branched biennial (or short-lived perennial) soft wooly silver-gray leaves and stems to 2' tall x 1'. Self sows if flowers are allowed to go to seed. 1" neon purple-red flowers open one at a time & last only a day, throughout **spring and summer**. Lychnis, is Greek for 'lamp': the felt-like leaves were formerly used for lamp wicks.
mid high	Dwarf Azalea (pink) *Rhododendron azalea* 'Rukisan'	(Klovey is a sport of Rukisan, so the description is probably much the same, except for size and color) 4"x12" in 10 yrs.
mid high & thru-out	White Diamond Sedum *Sedum pachyclados*	Tight, powder blue, glaucous evergreen foliage on short, spreading stems. 2" tall; non-invasive. Many light pink star flowers in **summer**.
mid high	Cobweb Hen & Chicks Sempervivum arachnoideum 'Spumanti'	Repeated.

	COMMON & BOTANICAL NAME	NOTES
mid high	White Mountain heather *Cassiope mertensiana*	NWN evergreen from 4 to 12". Short, erect, snakelike stems covered in tiny leathery scalelike leaves. From between the layers of scale leaves emerge reddish pedicels each bearing a petite, hanging, down-facing, bell-shaped flowers in **July**. The bractlets are red and the contrasting flower is white.
mid high	Cobweb Hen & Chicks *Sempervivum arachnoideum* 'Spumanti'	Repeated.
mid middle	Alpine Avens *Geum montanum*	Low growing alpine with dark green, pinnate leaves and deep yellow flowers **spring to summer**. 6" x 12".
mid middle	Dwarf Balsam Fir *Abies balsamea* 'Piccolo'	Tiny, radiating, dark green needles arch downward on many short, nearly vertical branches. Prominent brown buds highlight the branch tips on the dense, very dwarf globe. 2-3' in 10 yrs.
mid low	Dwarf Hinoki False Cypress *Chamaecyparis obtusa* 'DaintyDoll'	An irregular, upright, dwarf conifer to 4'x2' in 10 yrs. Very fine, lacy dark-green foliage. Prefers sun/partial shade in well-drained soil.
mid low	Hens & Chicks *Jovibarba heuffelii*	Evergreen succulent forms a mat of large rosettes, with light yellow blooms in **summer**. 8"x12". Grow in full sun, in poor, gritty, well drained soil.
through out	Foxglove *Digitalis purpurea*	Basal foliage with 3-4 ft tall flower spikes. Native to Europe; perennial, self seeds; poisonous—used to make heart medicine digitalis.
mid middle	Candytuft *Iberis sempervirens, cv*	Evergreen subshrub slowly spreads to form a tidy 6-12" x 1-3' cushion of shiny dark green leaves covered by flattened clusters of 4-petaled snow-white flowers in **late spring – early summer.**
mid low	Small Solomon Seal *Polygonatum biflorum*	Upright, arching, woodland plant of unbranched stems. Small, bell-shaped, greenish yellow flowers (usually in pairs) on short pedicels dangle in **spring** from the leaf axils along and underneath the arching stems. Flowers are followed by blue-black berries in autumn and leaves turn yellow.
mid above	Stonecrop *Sedum* 'Hot Stuff'	Tight, upright mound of blue-green foliage topped w/ bright, purple-pink flower clusters in **late summer**. Strong stems stay erect. 10-12"x12-15".
mid above	Prostrate Nordman Fir *Abies nordmanniana* 'Prostrata'	Dense, flat, blunt, dark green needles cover branches and have 2 whitish bands underneath. Slow-growing with a prostrate habit. 1 ft x 6 ft
mid high	Stonecrop *Sedum* 'Crystal Pink'	12"x 16" icy-pink flower heads, blue-green foliage.
mid high	Adriatic Bellflower *Campanula garganica* 'Dickson'sGold'	2"x 12" clumping mound of golden, heart-shaped leaves with star-shaped blue flowers thoughout the **summer**. Not aggressive like other garganicas, so does not 'hold its own' against larger perennials. Sun to part shade.

	COMMON & BOTANICAL NAME	NOTES
mid high	White Diamond Sedum *Sedum pachyclados*	Repeated.
mid high	Dwarf Norway Spruce *Picea abies* 'Clanbrassiliana Stricta'	A rounded shrub, becoming conical with age; short-needled dark green foliage . Grows to approx 1 ft in 10 years (some sites say matures to 3-4 ft).
mid high	Dwarf Balsam Fir *Abies balsamea* 'Nana'	Evergreen shrub, dwarf-18 to 30", globose form, top may flatten some with age, dense habit, branches outspread; needles 4-10 mm long, dark green, white stomatal lines below.
mid middle	Candytuft *Iberis sempervirens, cv*	Evergreen subshrub slowly spreads to form a tidy 6-12" x 1-3' cushion of shiny dark green leaves covered by flattened clusters of 4-petaled snow-white flowers in **late spring – early summer.**
mid middle	Maidenhair Fern *Adiantum aleudicum*	Deciduous NW native - wire-thin dark brown to purplish-black stems rising 12-18" tall, topped with a flattened "palm" of delicate fronds.
mid middle	Dwarf Siberian Spruce *Picea omorika* 'Pimoko'	Dark green needles accented with a bluish cast and silvery undersides. Reddish brown buds. Globe-shaped when young; multiple leaders & a upright, broad shape w/ maturity. 3-5 ft in 10 yrs (some sites say 1 ft in 10 yrs)
west middle	Fairy's Thimbles *Campanula cochlearfolia* 'BavarianBlue'	Small, heart-shaped, bright green leaves and many dark blue flowers in **summer.** Sun to part shade, moist, well-drained soil. 4" x 12"
west middle	Fern-leaf Bleeding Heart *Dicentra* 'King of Hearts'	Vigorous clump of powdery grey-green leaves, topped by clusters of delicate, dangling heart shaped flowers in a bright rose-red shade. Blooms **spring thru summer** if dead-headed.
mid low	Mossy Saxifrage *Saxifraga hypnoides*	A mossy saxifrage that makes carpet of tight, bright green rosettes with sprays of star white flowers to 4-10" high in **spring.** Part shade in poor, well drained soil.
mid low	Sea Holly *Eryngium bourgati*	Spiny-leafed rosette forming plant w/erect, thistle-like, leafy stalks bearing tight, steely-blue flowers in **mid-summer.**
mid low	Slender Deutzia *Deutzia* 'Nikko'	Deciduous shrub, tiny white **spring** flowers; dwarf, bronze fall color; to 30".
	WEST SECTION	From Prostrate Nordman Fir to entrance road at end of bed; shade.
west above	Copper Beech *Fagus sylvatica* 'Purpurea Group	Large deciduous tree located above and back. Deep red/purple leaves; beautiful orange fall color. Has small three-cornered nuts enclosed in spiny husks.
west above	Repeated 'Hot Stuff' Sedum and Mountain Laurel	

	COMMON & BOTANICAL NAME	NOTES
west above	Miniature Hinoki False Cypress *Chamaecyparis obtusa* 'Hage'	Dwarf, spherical and dark green. Some brown coloration in cold seasons. Blunt, paired leaves with 'X' markings underneath. Full sun. moist soil in cooler climate; 1ftx1ft/10 yrs.
west above	Bishop's Hat *Epimedium x rubrum*	Perennial, shade groundcover, pink/red blooms, bronze leaves in **summer/fall**.
west above	Lenten Rose *Helleborus orientalis*	
west high	Fern-leaf Bleeding Heart *Dicentra* 'King of Hearts'	Repeated.
west high	Weeping Hemlock *Tsuga canadensis* 'Cole's Prostrate'	Soft green ½" needles in a spiral arrangement on slender stems contrasting w/whitish gnarled bark. Grows slowly, 1.5 ftx3 ft in 10 yrs, spreading flat on the ground or cascading over walls.
west high	Oregon Stonecrop *Sedum oreganum*	Low, spreading mat of succulent green leaves, like a tiny Jade Plant. Yellow starry flowers appear in **summer**. Evergreen. During the **summer**, plants turn a bright crimson-red colour when grown in full sun, with lean dry soil. NW native particularly suited to areas with high precipitation.
west middle	Dwarf Hinoki False Cypress *Chamaecypris obtusa* 'Nana'	Dwarf pyramidal form of the species with compact foliage in shell-like sprays and a mature size of 2-3' tall.
west mid & thruout	Coral Bells *Heuchera cv.*	Herbaceous perennial; evergreen; Saxifrage family. Light green clump of evergreen leaves w/ small red bell-shaped flowers on slender 1 ft stems.
west middle	Various Sedum Sempervivum	Various Sedum Sempervivum cover this area, specific varieties are unknown.
west middle	Snow in Summer Cerastium tomentosum	Light grey-green cushion of evergreen foliage to 8", covered with white flowers in **early summer**. Extremely xeric once established. Can be sheared or mowed after bloom to maintain dense habit the rest of the season.
west middle	Dwarf Rhododendron	
west low	Dwarf Japanese Holly *Ilex crenata* 'Dwarf Pagoda'	Broadleaf evergreen shrub, 2 ft tall (in Oregon a 25 year-old plant is 5 ft tall), very compact, dense, rounded, irregular horizontal branching. Leaves alternate, simple, small, rounded, very short internodes.
west low	Gentian Speedwell *Veronica gentianoides*	Mat of basal oblong-lanceolate, slightly toothed, glossy, dark green leaves in rosette form. Pale blue with darker blue veining, cup-shaped flowers on 12" long racemes **late spring thru early summer** if deadheaded.
west low	*Saxifraga x elisabethae* 'Icicle'	Yellow flowers in **late winter/early spring** above long needled, grey-green rosettes.

	COMMON & BOTANICAL NAME	NOTES
west low	Autumn Gentian (white/blue) *Gentiana sino ornata* 'Stardust'	Creeping grass-like foliage with trumpet-shaped white flowers with striking blue spotting in **autumn**. 3" x 8" Cool sun to part shade, rich, well-drained soil, regular water.
west middle & low	Partridge Foot *Lutkea pectinata*	Mat-forming, bright evergreen groundcover 6" high with finely divided leaves and spikes of white flower clusters. Adapts well to part shade with regular water.
West Middle	*Corydalis flexuosa* 'Blue Panda'	Plants form a clump of elegant, lacy, light green leaves, bearing upright stems with dangling tubular electric-blue flowers from **spring to fall** – does not go summer dormant like most varieties. 8" x 8".
west middle	*Rhododerdron campylognum myrtilloides*	Dwarf to 1 ft. thimble shaped plum purple nodding flowers on long pedicels in **May-June**.
west middle	Mountain Snowbells *Soldanella montana*	An evergreen member of the Primrose family it has multiple stems to 10" bearing sweet fringed lavender bells in **Mar-April**.
west middle	Myrtle or Creeping Spurge *Euphorbia myrsinites L.*	Blue-grey pointed leaves on spurge spikes to 14". Sulfur yellow flowers in **spring**. Slightly toxic-produces blisters on skin. A noxious weed in some states. Banned in CO.
west middle	Autumn Gentian (white) *Gentiana sino ornata* 'Moonlight'	Creeping grass-like foliage with trumpet-shaped pure white flowers in autumn. 3" x 8" Cool sun to part shade, rich, well-drained soil, regular water.
west above	*Rhododendron pseudochrysanthum*	A dwarf, 2'x2', compact dome shaped shrub with small gray-green leaves. Bell-shaped, pale pink flowers in **April**.
west above	*Rhododendron pachysanthum*	Silvery blue covering (tomentum) on the upper leaf surface, and tan wooly indumentum underneath the leaves that is silvery white on the young growth. Distinctive leaves and free flowering pinky white flowers in **April** form a neat rounded truss.
west above	*Rhododendron* 'Berg's Queen Bee'	Dwarf rhododendron with small green leaves with deep brown indumentum on the undersides. New foliage comes out as soft white before hardening to green. Light pink buds fading to white flowers in the **spring**.
west above	*Bergenia cordifolia* 'Eroica	Bright rose-pink flower clusters are held on sturdy red stems above the shiny, cabbage-like leaves in **early spring**. In the fall the leaves turn striking burgundy and provide lasting beauty into winter.
west above	Heartleaf Bergenia *Bergenia cordifolia*	Perennial, large heart-shaped leaf turns bronze in fall and winter, pink flowers in **winter**.
west above	*Pulmonaria, cvs* Including 'Dark Vader'	
west middle	*Allium cernuum*	
west middle	Yellow spring crocus	

	COMMON & BOTANICAL NAME	NOTES
west low	Blue Autumn Gentian *Gentiana sino ornata*	Creeping grass-like foliage with trumpet-shaped blue flowers in **autumn**. 3" x 8" Cool sun to part shade, rich, well-drained soil, regular water.
west low	*Jeffersonia Dubia*	Leaves kidney-shaped or nearly circular, 4-6 cm wide, margin somewhat sinuous, glaucous violet when young. Flowers 2-3 cm wide, light lavender-blue, with five to seven broadly ovate petals.
west end	Cornell Pink Rhododendron *R. mucrunulatum* 'Cornell Pink'	**Early spring** pink flowers before the leaves; developed at Cornell University.
west end	Koreanspice Viburnum *Viburnum carlesii*	Very fragrant flowers in dome-shaped heads in **early spring**.
west end	Mollis Azalea *Rhododendron x kosteranum*	Deciduous, yellow/orange blooms.
west end	*Tiarella* 'HappyTrails', Appalachian Trail', 'Jeepers Creepers', 'Pirate's Patch'	All varieties with a trailing/creeping habit.
west end above	*Cyclamen hederifolium*	In **fall**, mottled flowers emerge directly from the soil, followed by a carpet of patterned, mid- to dark green leaves variegated with patterns in white or silver lasting well into the next spring. Can bloom for up to two months. Each small pink or white flower has swept-back petals resembling a dove in flight, marked with maroon at the mouth.
west end above	Foamy Bells *Heucherella* 'Alabama Surprise'	12" tall. In spring & summer, leaves are gold with sharply contrasting red veining, then green up but retain the red veining. In fall & winter, it turns warm orange-pink. Small white flowers **late spring**.
west end above	Coral Bells *Heuchera* 'Southern Comfort'	14" plant changes its leaf color from cinnamon peach to burnished copper to amber. The large, lobed leaves give a bold, lush appearance, and are graced by creamy white flowers in **late summer**.

❧ LOWER WOODLAND -Wooded area above Rock Garden--includes Henry's Walking Trail (a wood-chip trail accessed at landing above the Gate Lodge Stairs.

GARDEN NOTES

This area is newly created and although some planting has been made, a list has not. The intent is to recreate an area representative of the many trails Henry forged through the 46 acres of his property. Woodland and NW native plants will predominate.

	COMMON & BOTANICAL NAME	NOTES

UPPER WOODLAND -Wooded area bordered by the Entry Band, Glade and Entrance-Woodland Beds. Henry's Walking Trail (woodchipped) winds through the Upper and Lower Woodlands and is accessed from the ADA parking spaces or from the landing above the Gate Lodge stairs.

GARDEN NOTES

This area is newly created and although some planting has been made, a list has not. The intent is to recreate an area representative of the many trails Henry forged through the 46 acres of his property. Woodland and NW native plants will predominate.

	COMMON & BOTANICAL NAME	NOTES

🦋 **ENTRY BANK** - The entrance drive area, from the top of the hill near the ADA parking spaces, over to the parking lot, and down the drive to the Gate Lodge entry drive. It includes the rock retaining wall below the Glade and the low stone wall extending around to the Rock Garden.

GARDEN NOTES
Reclamation of this area began in 2011 in connection with the development of the Woodland Areas – it is ongoing, so the list is not complete. Development of the Upper & Lower Woodland areas, that this bed borders, was begun in late 2009 and continues. The intent is to return this area to mostly woodland plants and West Coast natives – Henry Pittock's preference. The project includes the recreation of an original wood-chip trail through both the Upper and Lower Woodland area; 'Henry's Trail' starts behind the handicap parking and connects with the walk at the mid-landing of the stairs across from the Gate Lodge.

	COMMON & BOTANICAL NAME	NOTES
	Gold-leaved Red Current *Ribes sanguineum* 'Brocklebankii'	Shrub w/light yellow-green leaves. Flowers in **early spring** followed by edible berries in mid-summer
though-out	Ferns	Over 360 in North America - many varieties throughout the grounds In this bed: 'Lady' (tallest), 'Bracken' (under Vine Maple), 'Sword', 'Maiden Hair',
through-out bank	Daffodil *Narcissus*	Decendent of wild narcissus. Yellow flowers in **spring** on a single stem, have a central trumpet (cup) longer than the petals
through-out	Pacific Coast Iris, cvs	'Coastal Glow', butter yellow; Hidden Asset',tan mahogany blend w/pink highlights; Munras', drk cream yellow; 'Wild Survivor', light med blue.
	Vine Maple *Acer circinatum*	Native, deciduous, understory multi-stemmed tree; yellow fall color in shade, red in sun.
	Oregon Grape *Mahonia aquifolium*	Shrub w/shiny, holly-shaped green leaves; bronze-burgandy in winter. Bright yellow flowers in **spring** (Oregon State flower), then blue berry-like fruit.
	Redtwig Dogwood *Cornus sericea*	Shrub w/red stems on new growth that provide winter interest.
	Witch Hazel *Hamamelis x intermedia* 'Arnold's Promise'	Shrub or small tree with an open, spreding form to 15-20ftH x 10-18ft W. Fragrant yellow star-shaped flowers on branches **before leaves appear**. Bright green foliage turns yellow in fall.
	Midwinter Fire Dogwood *Cornus sanguinea* 'Midwinter Fire'	6'x6' deciduous shrub w/winter stems ranging from red at tips to orange to yellow at base. Creamy white flowers followed by red fruit that attracts birds.
	Common Snowberry *Symphoricarpus albus*	Native deciduous rhizomatous shrub to 6';small pink-white flowers in **early summer**. White fruits in winter, bend the branches to the ground.
	Stewartia	

	COMMON & BOTANICAL NAME	NOTES
	Coral Bells *Heuchera*	
	Western Azalea *Azalea occidentale*	Deciduous shrub to 6 ft x5 ft. Has fragrant white, tinged pink flowers, with yellow blotch in **May**. Foliage turns orange-red in fall.
	Mountain Ash *Sorbus*	
	Purple Ninebark *Physocarpus opulifolius* 'Diabolo'	Upright deciduous shrub, 10 × 10 ft. Leaves purplish-red during much of the growing season, needs sun to maintain color. White flowers and reddish fruit. Peeling bark provides winter interest.
through-out	*Heuchera, Heucherella, Tiarella*	
	Birchleaf Spirea *Spirea betulifolia* 'Tor'	3' x 3' mound of dark gray-green birch-like leaves changing to shades of orange, red, and purple in the fall. Covered w/tiny white flowers in **spring**.
	Korean Dogwood *Cornus Kousa*	
	Harry Lauder's Walking Stick Corkscrew Hazel *Corylus avallana* 'Contorta'	Upright, tree-like shrub to 10-15 ft x 10-15 ft; heart-shaped, toothed, mid-green leaves. Pendent yellow catkins in **late winter and early spring**. Strongly twisted, spiraling shoots provide year-round interest.
	Point Reyes Creeper *Ceanothus gloriosus* 'Point Reyes'	Low evergreen groundcover with blue flowers. Very drought tolerant. Shiny, dark green leaves, about 1 inch long. 6"-12" h x 1-12 ft wide.
	Helleborus	

GARDEN TOURS AT PITTOCK MANSION

Free tours of the Pittock Mansion gardens are offered by Master Gardeners on select Saturdays throughout the summer months. Take a stroll around the beautiful gardens of this historic mansion overlooking the city of Portland and enjoy these informal garden conversations with OSU-trained Master Gardeners. Learn about the history of the gardens, the fascinating legacy of Henry and Georgiana Pittock and the ever-changing design of the Mansion grounds.

Henry Pittock loved maples and called their hilltop property "Maple Grove." A variety of maples are planted to reflect that theme. Many roses have also been planted in honor of Georgiana Pittock, considered the Grandmother of the Rose Festival. Georgiana hosted early rose competitions in her front garden at the Pittock's original home in downtown Portland. The Pittock Mansion gardens are also home to native evergreens, perennial borders, shade and rock gardens.

The free garden tours are offered on the second and fourth Saturdays of the month, June through September. OSU Master Gardener volunteer guides are available from 11:00 a.m.– 2:00 p.m, to give garden tours or to answer your gardening questions. No advance reservations are required and the tours are wheelchair accessible.

-Amy Waldron, OSU Master Gardener,
Pittock Mansion Garden Tour Director

Metro area Master Gardener™ Extension Office

Volunteers from the OSU Extension Service Master Gardener™ program provide relevant, research-based education and outreach to the public of Clackamas, Multnomah, and Washington Counties about horticulture and household pests. This information promotes sustainable practices that minimize risks to human health and the environment.

CONTACT INFORMATION

Clackamas County

Phone: 503–655–8631
Email: clackmg@oregonstate.edu
Address: 200 Warner–Milne Rd. Oregon City, OR 97045
Hours: 9 AM – 12 Noon and 1 PM – 4 PM, Monday – Friday

Multnomah County

Phone: 503–445–4608
Email: mcmastergardeners@yahoo.com
Address: 2701 NW Vaughn St. Suite 450 Portland, OR 97210
Hours: 10 AM – 2 PM, Monday – Friday

Washington County

Phone: 503–821–1150
Email: mastergardener.wc@oregonstate.edu
Address: Public Services Building, 155 N. First Avenue, Suite #200, Hillsboro, OR 97124-3072
Hours: 9 AM –12 PM and 1 PM – 4 PM, Monday – Friday

If you live outside of this geographic area, please find your local Cooperative Extension office.

Oregon State University Extension Service offers educational programs, activities, and materials without discrimination based on age, color, disability, gender identity or expression, marital status, national origin, race, religion, sex, sexual orientation, or veteran's status. Oregon State University Extension Service is an Equal Opportunity Employer.

Additional Copies of this book are available at:

The Museum Store at Pittock Mansion,
open daily during Mansion hours of operation and
shop remains one half hour later.

Pittock Mansion
3229 NW Pittock Dr Portland, OR 97210
website: pittockmansion.org
Mansion: 503-823-3623
Museum Store: 503-823-3628

Hours:
February 1st - June 30: 11:00 am to 4:00 pm Daily
July 1 - August 31: 10 am to 5 pm Daily
September 1 - December 31 Daily*

Closed on:
* November: the weekend preceding Thanksgiving (Friday through Sunday)
*Thanksgiving Day
*Christmas Day
January 1 - 31.

Made in the USA
Charleston, SC
18 May 2013